# NO WORD FOR
# WILDERNESS

# No Word for Wilderness

Italy's Grizzlies and the Race to
Save the Rarest Bears on Earth

Roger Thompson

Ashland
Creek
Press

To Margaret,
Save the bears!

No Word for Wilderness
Italy's Grizzlies and the Race to Save the Rarest Bears on Earth
By Roger Thompson

Published by Ashland Creek Press
Ashland, Oregon
www.ashlandcreekpress.com

ISBN 978-1-61822-056-1
Library of Congress Control Number: 2017956556

Cover photograph of an Abruzzo bear by Bruno D'Amicis
www.brunodamicis.com

*For Ethan*

who would not let me forget about the bears of Abruzzo

# Contents

Banff and Reno ................................................................ 1

Part I: A Tale of Two Bears ........................................... 7
   Wilderness and Italy's Alpine Bears ............................. 9
   Italy's Ancient Bears ..................................................... 15

Part II: Orso Bruno ........................................................ 21
   A Time to Make Friends ............................................... 23
   A Bear Is Born ............................................................... 31
   Petzi ................................................................................ 35
   Bruno Attacks ............................................................... 43
   The Hunt for Bruno ...................................................... 49
   Taunt .............................................................................. 55
   Bruno, Enemy of the State ............................................ 61

Part III: The Last Bears of Abruzzo ............................. 67
   Italian Grizzlies ............................................................. 69
   Endangered Lives and Livelihoods ............................... 77
   Classifying Hope ............................................................ 83
   *Ursus arctos marsicanus* ............................................... 89
   The King Who Launched a Movement ........................ 99
   Hagiography ................................................................... 105

Erasure......................................................................... 109

Control .......................................................................... 115

Part IV: Bandits and Bureaucracy................................. 123

Smoke........................................................................... 125

Ambush ........................................................................ 133

*Uso Civico* .................................................................... 143

Fade Out....................................................................... 149

Pax Romana and the "Nature Tax" ............................. 155

The Cows of Little Tibet ............................................. 161

The Blue Snow of Abruzzo .......................................... 167

Rewilding the Mob ...................................................... 177

Part V: Resurrecting the Wild....................................... 185

Save the Bears .............................................................. 187

Loi and Loss................................................................. 191

Beautiful Minds ........................................................... 197

Ark................................................................................ 205

Part VI: Father Bear...................................................... 211

Champions ................................................................... 213

The Limits of Science................................................... 219

Works Cited................................................................. 225

# Introduction:
# Banff and Reno

Not far from the blue waters of Lake Louise, we descended into a small meadow. I was hiking in Banff National Park with Reno Sommerhalder, a proud native of Switzerland who is an internationally recognized bear naturalist. A thoughtful, meditative, and persistent advocate for bears around the globe, he lectures on them frequently throughout Europe and has published well-received memoirs about his life among grizzlies. I knew taking a long walk with him in the Canadian Rockies in search of bears was bound to be an adventure.

We were only an hour or so into our hike when we decided to head off-trail to seek out the bears. Ahead of us was Mount Assiniboine Provincial Park, and the backcountry between it and the more popular areas of Banff promised ideal habitat for bears. Just before we turned west toward the border of British Columbia, however, a young woman emerged from behind a ridge and walked our way. When she was only a few meters away, she hailed us.

"Hello," she said. "It's a perfect day!"

She was right. The day had started with some cold, early morning mist, but the skies had cleared, and a bright sun was shining, warming us from an autumn breeze that was flowing down from nearby peaks.

Snow had already fallen in higher elevations, and that night, it would dust our tent as well, but now, midmorning in the fullness of the rich, sunny air, it seemed like a perfect day.

The young woman who called out to us was Vladmira Lackova, an outdoor enthusiast who has worked around the world in various nature parks. She is a native of Slovakia, and her Facebook feed looks like an adventure travel website. A savvy and experienced world traveler, she has set foot in more remote places than most of us could ever hope. That day, high in an alpine meadow in the shadow of Assiniboine, she would unwittingly change my life.

Vladmira told me that bears lived in Italy, an idea I found so disorienting that I expressed not just surprise but outright skepticism. She was, however, insistent. Not only are there bears in Italy, she said, but they are brown bears. She saw my incredulity and leaned toward me, cast her eyes around as though sharing a secret, and said with a mocking fake whisper something that to my mind made her claim cross into the realm of genuine absurdity.

They live, she said, barely an hour's drive from Rome.

I looked at Reno. Vladmira looked at Reno. I searched for some sign of a joke—two Euro-somethings playing tricks on the American in the Canadian Rockies—but it never came. Instead, there was only Vladmira's final assertion.

They are, she insisted, very, very special bears.

Reno echoed the sentiment, and I realized that he, too, knew about Italy's bears. Indeed, he knew them quite well. A wilderness guide, he leads bear observation trips around the globe and has been deeply involved in European bear campaigns. He ushers adventurers to Alaska, and he is one of the few people Russian officials permit to lead trips into Kamchatka to see the remarkable bears there. If you're an American, he's your only ticket to that part of the world. He is as conversant with bear conservation issues and as knowledgeable of different bear populations as anyone on Earth, so Vladmira's story about Italian bears was no surprise to him. He suggested it should not be to me either.

I did not know how to make sense of it. Brown bears were the stuff of remote wilderness and high mountains. How could they live so close to Rome? Yet they do, and they have for longer than any written record that exists. The history of Rome means absolutely nothing to them, and neither does their proximity to so many millions of people.

There are, of course, bears within an hour's drive of other major metropolitan areas around the world. Within an hour of Calgary or Denver you can find bears, and, if you're clever enough to know where to look, you might find them a short drive from San Francisco or LA. Certainly, not far from Seattle and Portland you can find bears aplenty. But outside of Rome seemed impossible to me. In some ways, it still does. Despite years of outdoor guiding and education, I had never heard about bears in Italy.

As it turns out, I am not alone. Anyone I have spoken to after that day in the Rockies seems as surprised as I was, and equally incredulous.

"Black bears?" many of them ask.

"No, brown bears," I say, usually following this with an anticipatory rebuttal: "I'm not joking."

Doubt is warranted, I think. We associate Italy with ancient history, Tuscan landscapes, great wine and food, astonishing art, religious and spiritual traditions, fierce pride in local customs, and any number of stereotypes about the people who now call themselves Italian Americans, but few of us conjure images of nature—at least in the sense of wilderness and the wild—when we think of Italy. The land is too old there, too saturated with human civilization, and too long developed by human industry and culture.

But brown bears persist there. Against all odds and in contradiction to what most of us think we know about human-animal interaction, they have found a way to survive in the face of one of humanity's oldest societies.

The journey to my understanding of this startling fact has been, predictably in hindsight, hardly straightforward, and this book is an attempt to try to suss it all out. My hope is that this book provides some sense of the history of the bears there while tracing in as clear a way as possible the complicated relationships between humans and animals in that part of the world. As a *forestiero*, the term some Italians use to label an outsider or even interloper, I recognize significant limitations to what I might accomplish. My ability to penetrate the richness and nuance of the Italian experience, let alone the extensive scientific work being done on behalf of the bears, is certainly worthy of some skepticism in its own right. To try to compensate, I relied throughout this project on the goodwill and genuine devotion of too many people to count. While stories shifted and changed as different people told me about their lives with the bears, it was rare that one story contradicted or undermined the truth of the incredibly complex issues surrounding conservation in Italy. Their different stories were like the various colors a prism casts, none outshining the other but each sparking from a central, crystalline truth, which is this: The bears in Italy need help.

It turns out that there is more than one population of brown bears in Italy, and understanding the distinction between the two—one the last vestige of a former time that persists against all odds and the other a great experiment in rewilding that, if successful, promises to change how we see not only Italy but all of Europe—is one of the aims of this book. To understand that distinction is to face difficult questions about the possibility for relocating "wild," large mammals in places like Europe. It is also, however, to encounter promising opportunities for reshaping natural environments all over the world. Italy provides a compelling case study that has been a millennium in the making, and there are surely few comparable experiments in beast-human cohabitation to Italy's with bears. If we can make sense of that example and if we can generalize to even the slightest degree what Italy's bears can teach us, we will be equipped to carry out fundamental changes in how humans and animals interact and live together.

Those opportunities seem to me at a critical point. We may well be at a "now or never" moment. The stories in both central Italy, where one set of bears lives, and northern Italy, where the other set lives, are changing, and time is, by most accounts, growing short to make a difference. Yet with more discussion about Italy's bears and greater understanding of what it takes to maintain—and even rethink—wild space in a decidedly settled land, lasting change is possible. The people who have dedicated years of their lives to saving the Italian bears may finally receive the backing they need to do their work, and if so, they may finally be able to carry their wisdom from the quiet corners of rural Italy to the broader world of conservation. Theirs is a lesson that we all need to hear.

# PART I: A TALE OF TWO BEARS

# 1

~~~

# Wilderness and Italy's Alpine Bears

He claims he was minding his own business when he was attacked. Daniele Maturi says he had been foraging for mushrooms just north of the village of Pinzolo, Italy, when he spotted the bear. It was a female with two cubs, and, according to Maturi, the beast did not provide an opportunity for him to retreat. She simply attacked, knocking him to the ground and taking vicious swipes at him. She ripped at his leg and foot and pressed him into the ground with her great forepaws. Maturi tried to roll away, clawing at the ground to pull himself from the attacking animal. He was certain he was about to be killed, and as he struggled, he became more desperate to get away. He hit the bear, striking her snout, then reached out on the forest floor, trying to find rocks and branches, anything he could use as a weapon. He escaped only when the bear unexpectedly stopped her attack and returned to her cubs, trotting away into the woods and leaving him behind, bloodied and broken.

Maturi moved as quickly as he could to get out of the forest. A gash down his left leg hampered him, but when he finally emerged, he was conveyed to a hospital and treated for his wounds. The physical trauma was not as extensive as it could have been. No major organs or arteries had been damaged, and aside from the slashing wounds from the claws, the bear had done little else to hurt him. She had not bitten him, and she had not broken any of his bones or torn flesh from his body. Despite the emotional trauma from the encounter, Maturi had been, in many respects, fortunate. A wild brown bear is capable of killing a man with a single blow to the head or neck. He walked away relatively unscathed.

The attack on Maturi in August of 2014 was from a relatively well-known bear named Daniza, who until the attack had been known as a quiet and peaceful animal. Despite her positive history, sensationalized news stories quickly filled newspapers after the attack, condemning the bear. Media flooded the area to cover the event. One report announced "Bear Attack!" Another, quoting the victim, ran the headline, "I Was Afraid I Would Die!" By July of 2015, the province of Trentino, where the attack occurred, was calling for a cull of "dangerous bears," even though the proclamation offered little guidance in how to identify and locate such bears. Taken as a whole, the stories about the attack and about bears in the area led inevitably to one idea: The only good bear is a dead bear.

At the same time, local environmental groups launched an offensive aimed at redirecting outrage over the event. Daniele Maturi became the subject of sustained personal attacks on his character. He went by the nickname "Carnera," a reference to an Italian boxer and movie star, and seemed to some too eager to be in the spotlight. Protests erupted outside his apartment, and he began receiving death threats online and through the mail when his contact information was made public. One postcard, postmarked from Bologna, punned on the scientific name for a grizzly bear, *Ursus arctos horribilis*, in order to make its point: "We wish you a year horribilis, to happen to you about as bad you can imagine so that Daniza and her children will be avenged. It was all your fault, mushroom picker with no other work. Stay at home!"

Various groups began to question Maturi's account of the attack, in particular the idea that he simply stumbled on the bear while out looking for mushrooms and that he had fought off the bear with his bare fists. They called him a liar, referred to his nickname as evidence of his overblown sense of self-importance, and argued that no real investigation of Maturi's claims was ever made. The implication was that he simply made up the entire attack and that local officials were complicit in a cover-up.

The reason?

For many who doubted Maturi's story, it all came down to money. He was, they claimed, the employee of a ski resort whose plans for expansion were halted because Daniza was known to have cubs that were ranging in the proposed development area. With Daniza out of the way, the environmentalists argued, the ski resort could return to its plans to build more slopes and more condominiums. For them, Maturi was the boob sent to do the bidding of the developers: Demonize a bear in order to remove it from the area and thus pave the way for the resort expansion.

Daniza was part of a bear reintroduction campaign in the Alps that was controversial from the outset. Life Ursus, a program sponsored by the European Union, was an attempt to repopulate central Europe with wild brown bears. The Life Ursus team studied various possibilities for a reintroduction plan and determined that the Italian Alps provided ideal habitat for new bears and that a particular group of eastern European brown bears had the best chance to make the transition to Italy. They culled animals from a thriving population in Slovenia, where bears in some areas outnumber people, handpicking males and females who presented the best opportunity for procreation.

Slovenia has a remarkably large and diverse bear population. Some estimates put the number around 2,000 bears, so the choice to import bears from Slovenia seemed obvious. The bears are abundant and healthy there, and taking a small group of both males and females over a period of years would likely have little effect on the remaining population. So, in 1999 and then again in 2000, the project managers, measured in their approach but optimistic in their plan, trapped ten Slovenian bears and transported them to northern Italy.

The bears' new home, the Adamello-Brenta Provincial Park, is renowned for its beauty and surprising wildness. Situated just over a mountain range from the growing city of Trento, the park boasts more than fifty lakes in an area under 500 square miles and bridges two major ranges of the Italian Alps: the Brenta Dolomites group and the granite Adamello-Presanella massif. Between the ranges runs the Sarca River. The valleys that rise up from the river are dotted with villages and ski slopes. High mountains, some reaching more than 9,000 feet, ring ancient glaciers. Streams course down from the mountains and feed verdant fields below.

The park is an extension of an area called the Dolomites, a UNESCO World Heritage site of stunning natural beauty and ancient history. Marmots screech their calls into the wind throughout the summer, and the elusive ptarmigan struts across windblown snowbanks in the winter. Marten scavenge along creeks, and chamois leap from rock to rock in scree fields and rugged canyons. Impressive castles and forts perch on hilltops, highlighting the fact that the region has witnessed tides of cultural change brought by war, trade, and shifting national and provincial boundaries. During World War I, a secret fortress was built high in the mountains, complete with countless tunnels and hidden lairs, and during World War II, the area became part of an underground network of passageways for Jews escaping the Holocaust. The local dialect reflects ongoing changes in culture and influence, with some citizens in the area speaking German, others Italian, and still others a remnant language, Ladin, whose roots are long since forgotten. The language sounds like a cross between Italian and German, but Roman vestiges suggest that a heritage from Italy's capital colors the linguistic oddity. It is as unique to the area as Creole is to parts of Louisiana, and thousands still speak it.

Brown bears have always favored the area, so officials expected the Slovenian bears to adapt well to their new home, but Life Ursus's introduced bears thrived beyond all expectation. By 2005, dozens of cubs had been born, and the mountains were once again home to brown bears. Headlines like "The Great Bear Comeback" ran in *Der Spiegel*, Germany's equivalent to the *New York Times*, and project managers spoke openly about their hope for further expansion. They cited the fact that the bears had already ventured outside the reintroduction area, and in 2004, they noted, bears began to move into Austria. In May of 2005, a wild bear set foot in Switzerland for the first time in more than 100 years, making a grand entrance by wandering into a village where sightseers and well-wishers got startlingly close to the animal to take pictures. One Swiss paper ran the headline, "THE BEAR IS BACK!" The enthusiasm was palpable.

But it was not universal. Not everyone was thrilled with the idea of bears returning to the Alps. Opponents of the reintroduction campaign voiced skepticism that bears from another country would be able to live in Italy without disrupting human activity, and the program ignited wide debate in Italy about the significance of wildlife to cultural identity.

Despite the fact that in the second half of the twentieth century Italy led the world in the establishment of nature parks, the average Italian's experience with nature remains couched in a centuries-old preference for human settlement. The image of a pristine natural habitat hardly features in the Italian cultural imagination, even though the country witnessed a virtual explosion of park creation. Most Italians have little sense of how their country stacks up to preservation attempts across Europe and the world, highlighting the fundamental truth that Italian culture has rarely prized nature conservation.

More than one writer has pointed out that the Italian language has no word for *wilderness*. There is no direct translation of the word—or even of the idea. Most translations derive from words for forests or woodland, but *wilderness* in the way that much of the rest of the West imagines it has no clear referent. It is not a concept that carries significant cultural currency and thus has never really needed a word. There is no strong nature writing or eco-poetry tradition in Italy, nor is there a widely recognized tradition of pastoral painting or landscape photography. In Italy there is no Thoreau equivalent any more than there is an Ansel Adams. This is not to say that there are not important practitioners or artists in those fields, but as far as an established and widely recognized tradition, Italy is stunningly silent.

This is a reflection of a pretty basic fact: Italy represents human achievement, not untouched wilderness. In a country where culture and the arts continue to receive serious consideration from many quarters of the population, very few native Italians have any desire to visit the wilderness or experience "the wild" in the way that Arctic or Alaskan or Siberian explorers might. Such a thing sounds quaintly American, or, perhaps, northern European. "Roughing it" or "sleeping under the stars" is something that people of the hinterlands do. The Italians spent a thousand years clearing the land to ensure they would never again have to struggle with the wild, and the memory of the time before, when vandals and tribal warlords raided the countryside and great beasts roamed the woods, is etched into the Italian mind. One senses its presence in the villages perched on hilltops and the massive walls surrounding many of the cities to this day. They are daily reminders of human triumph over the natural world and persistent evidence of human triumph over forest and mountain predators. Human advancement meant conquest of nature—and its wild animals.

Especially bears.

# 2

~

# Italy's Ancient Bears

Italy has always had bears. At one time, the massive cave bear roamed northern parts of the country before the species died out. Other types of bears, though, persisted, and even in Roman times, bears were part of the culture. At that time, they were routinely rounded up and transported to cities where they would be dropped into coliseums to fight other animals, warriors, or criminals for the entertainment of the masses. Etchings and frescoes document the hunting and trapping of bears as well as the ritualistic slaughtering of them in front of crowds. By the Renaissance, the bears became prized quarry for noblemen on hunting excursions, and aristocrats maintained country homes (more like mini-palaces) in order to hunt and celebrate their adventures in the mountains and woods. By the turn of the twentieth century, bears had been almost entirely eliminated from the Italian peninsula.

Remnant populations of them, however, lingered in high mountain passes and hidden forest glens. Some roamed the Alps, where human settlement was thinner than in the piedmont of Italy, and the animals lived largely unmolested for most of the twentieth century.

In northern Italy, the brown bear was, at one time, a point of pride, so when the Life Ursus program first sought out places for a bear reintroduction campaign, the region seemed like an obvious area to investigate. Throughout the early and mid-twentieth century, the Italian Alps were home to a group of seventy native brown bears. There, they foraged and thrived, but as twentieth-century development inched further into the mountain valleys and up the slopes, the bears came into increasing contact with the encroaching human population. No significant problems were reported between man and beast, but still, the bears began to disappear, casualties of poaching and poisoning. By the 1990s, only three native northern brown bears were left; all others had been extirpated by human activity. The final native northern bear died in the early 2000s.

Another remnant brown bear population, though, found safe haven in central Italy, deep in the Apennine Mountains. The Apennines form the spine of Italy and stretch roughly north to south the entire length of the country. They extend southward from the Alps down along Tuscany and Umbria before descending out of Abruzzo into Campania and Calabria. There, the mountains meet the Ionian Sea in a space where the blue Adriatic sweeps around the heel of Italy and mingles with the Mediterranean in the instep of the country's geographic boot.

Bears ranged across the entire length of the Apennines for most of human history. As the human population grew and city-states thrived, though, they were eradicated from most parts of the mountains. Yet one small group of bears persisted, hidden among the crags and canyons in a largely forgotten land. Despite being hemmed in by population booms on the coasts of Italy, a single remnant of the ancient bears of the Apennines lives on, the last of their kind and the last ambassadors of an astonishing history. They live in Abruzzo, not fifty miles from Rome.

Abruzzo is home to high mountains and lush valleys, with stands of old-growth beech forests that escaped logging hidden among the foothills. In the early twentieth century, the impressive mountain landscape attracted a nascent alpine skiing movement and brought greater public awareness of the beauty of the central Apennines, but in general, the high mountainous landscape of Abruzzo remains a footnote in a country with too many historical and cultural treasures to count. The region shimmers like a mirage at the periphery of awareness, and, even among Italians, it is ephemeral.

Abruzzo is frequently seen as a backwater of sorts. Dialects of the region have come to represent the equivalent of a hillbilly or redneck accent in the States. Foreign tourists drift to Rome, Venice, or Florence, typically ignoring Abruzzo. In fact, most tourists coming from abroad have not even heard of the region, and those who have likely know it by its wine, Montepulciano d'Abruzzo, a rustic red that has enjoyed a recent spike in popularity thanks to an aggressive marketing campaign. Those few who do make it to the area are, for the most part, other Italians, and they typically head to the Adriatic coast instead of the mountains. They flood beach resorts in Pescara and Silvi Marina in the summer, enjoying the soft surf of the Adriatic. The beaches buzz with activity throughout the day from June through August as swimmers and gawkers alike mingle along the warm waters. At night, dancers and revelers fill nightclubs and bars. Abruzzo's mountains are far from the minds of most of the beach set even though Gran Sasso, the tallest mountain of the Apennine Peninsula, is fewer than thirty miles away and in clear view of some of the more popular Adriatic beaches.

For many Abruzzese, mountains define their culture, and their history is inextricably linked to a wilderness wedged between Rome and Greece. Living in the shadows of the mountains on the western boundaries of the region and in the salty air of the Adriatic on the eastern side, their story is itself a story of the land. They conceive of themselves as deeply connected to the earth and sea, and the result is that they have for generations found a natural balance that has flown in the face of the excesses of Rome.

Apennine bears developed a remarkably peaceful relationship with the people who call the Abruzzo mountains home. While the bears in the north of Italy to this day face ongoing conflict with local mayors and local farmers, the bears in the Apennines have enjoyed generations of quiet cohabitation with their human neighbors. The coexistence of man and animal here has been one of the great secrets of the natural world, as well as one of the great mysteries in the field of conservation. No one is quite sure how Abruzzo's human-bear relationship has been so successfully maintained.

The problematic perception of bears as aggressive beasts in northern Italy, however, seems to be spreading southward toward Abruzzo. New anxiety about bears has been stoked by stories about bear maulings like Daniza's in the north, and when sensationalistic reports emblazon front pages of newspapers, few readers—let alone the writers who craft the stories— care to draw distinctions between the bears in northern Italy and those in Abruzzo.

As a result, the image of the terrible bear has taken on increasing force in Italian reportage, and Abruzzo's bears are facing unwarranted threats from people who fear their existence. The slow disappearance of local farmers and shepherds from the region has only made matters worse. As the people who were born and raised among the mountain bears of Abruzzo pass away, their special relationship with the bears dies with them. Without their stories and without their history, Abruzzo's bears begin to seem like any other fearsome bear. They start to resemble the tall-tale grizzlies of the American West or the unduly maligned Slovenian bears now living in the Italian Alps. Dangerous beasts. Bloodthirsty predators who stalk humans. They begin to look like anything other than what they truly are—which is a bear unlike any other in the world.

The Abruzzo bears are not the same bears as in the north of the country. The bear that attacked Maturi in the Italian Alps was not an Abruzzo bear, and indeed as a transplanted Slovenian bear was one of a group of animals who are, by reputation, less likely to flee human contact and more likely to confront agitators than Italy's native bears. The Slovenian bears now living in the north of Italy seem to respond more aggressively to fear and survival, and instead of cowering to avoid conflict, they may lash out at or charge perceived threats. Though still less aggressive than the North American grizzly, they are nonetheless unafraid of a fight.

They are also ill-equipped to negotiate the complex relationship that has developed between Italians and wild animals. Raised in a land far from the place where they now live, they have hardly been embraced as an immutable fact of life in the Alps. Suspicion about their ability to live so close to people lingers even among their advocates, and without a tradition of true wilderness in the area, many people have found life with bears challenging.

And terrifying. Many people have a deep fear of wild animals of any stripe, let alone a brown bear. When stories of rampaging bears surface in the media, that primal human response wells up and is nurtured by horrific images and graphic descriptions. Bears seem inescapably dangerous.

Yet the persistence of the two types of bears in Italy suggests a different story. It suggests a story of reconciliation where the survival of wild animals and the survival of a people are inextricably linked. It suggests a story of coexistence with surprising acts of cooperation at its center. It suggests a parable whose lesson is the value of nature to human society. And ultimately, it suggests that Italy may again give us something of such lasting importance and such profound consequence that it could reshape our relationship with the natural world.

Hidden within its history and the story of its various bears, Italy has a new gift to offer the world, a concept of wilderness that is decidedly different than the idea of pure wild that dominates the cultural imagination about what constitutes wild spaces. The wilderness that persists in Abruzzo relies on human-beast interaction, and though it is ancient there, it is new to the rest of the world. This new wilderness can fundamentally change how humans live with animals around the world, but for many years, it has been missing one important feature.

Italy's special brand of wilderness has had no voice. Without it, Italy's bears and the special type of wild they represent have slowly slipped toward extinction.

But that has changed. There are voices now, and the story they are telling promises to change conservation in Italy and around the globe.

If, that is, they have not come too late.

# PART II: ORSO BRUNO

# 3

# A Time to Make Friends

The farmer had heard about the bear. Everyone had. The valley stirred with rumors about the violence of the attacks and the strangeness of seeing a wild bear roam the countryside, but he never thought *he'd* have to worry about it. A bear in Bavaria seemed impossible. What were the odds? But, on a brisk May morning in 2006, he woke up to find carnage in his livestock pen. The gate had been torn from its hinges, and twisted and contorted heaps of dead sheep were strewn about the enclosure. Some bore long slashes across their necks, and others had gaping belly wounds. The slain animals had not been eaten. They were simply slaughtered, and their bloody carcasses were tossed to the ground and left behind. Blood had turned the mud a ruddy brown.

The bear had come down out of the German Alps repeatedly over the last week, seeking out easy kills. He was becoming increasingly brazen in his attacks. No longer skirting the edges of villages, he was breaking into enclosures within the towns themselves, leaving behind wrecked pens and gruesome masses of dead animals. He never took an animal with him. He never returned to feast on his killings. Instead, he mauled his prey and, like a ghost, disappeared. The bear, it seemed to some, was killing solely for the sake of killing.

A story about a bear attacking sheep in the heart of Bavaria should have been insignificant, a local matter to be handled by local authorities. The idea that international media would care seemed almost absurd, and the first reports in newspapers across the country were thin, almost dismissively brief. But this was no ordinary bear, and this was no ordinary time. Germany was hosting the 2006 World Cup, and the international media was scouring the country for stories to broadcast to the world. They would latch onto the news of this particular beast, and, in doing so, make him more famous than any animal before him.

He was the first wild brown bear in Germany in more than 150 years, and he arrived in the country just as the World Cup was about to begin. Germany had won the right to host the great soccer tournament by only a single vote, beating out South Africa in a controversial voting process. Four years later, South Africa would finally win its bid for the games and become the first African nation to host the event, but in 2006, Germany wore the World Cup mantle and intended to silence critics by staging a historic competition. They planned to demonstrate that they had deserved that single vote and the selection. The bear would nearly ruin everything.

The country spent four years updating stadiums and building an infrastructure to support the hordes of fans. Twelve cities upgraded or built new venues, and the country spent $300 million alone on renovating Berlin's stadium. New hubs, terminals, and mass transit systems were built, ensuring that 50,000 fans per hour could be shuttled to and from each stadium. New roads cut across cities and the countryside, and innovative public transportation systems spread out across the country like a web in order to handle the surge of more than four million fans flooding the host nation. The planning was efficient and impressive, and it trickled down from municipal governments to residents. Glowing press discussing Germany's extraordinary preparations went out across the wires.

Throughout the spring of 2006, towns and villages also prepared.

Many set up viewing platforms in town squares where visitors could gather, drink, and view the games without paying the steep price for match tickets and without, officials hoped, fear of violence. Well-heeled locals set up inviting home rentals, catering to visitors and trying to make a dime on the fans. Sport kiosks popped up in every storefront, and children and adults alike felt the pull of entrepreneurship and began to sell trinkets to tourists, including shirts, shorts, towels, and coffee mugs emblazoned with a smiley-face logo with the event's motto: A Time to Make Friends.

The 2006 World Cup would ultimately become one of the most popular television events of all time, with nearly 27 billion viewers around the world, and the revenue from tourism and merchandise was in the tens of millions of dollars. Throughout May and in early June of 2006, all eyes had turned to Germany in anticipation of the greatest spectacle in the sporting world, and Germany seemed prepared. The new transportation systems hummed, ticket sales surged, and the government braced for the fan onslaught. Just as the first national soccer teams began to arrive for the competition, though, Germany had to turn its attention to a nuisance in the south of the country, a nuisance that eventually sparked an all-out crisis and drew much of the world's attention away from World Cup soccer. The German government, on the cusp of stunning international acclaim, found itself embroiled in an international controversy over a wild animal.

Deep in the mountains of Bavaria, a wild bear was on a rampage. The beast first set foot in Germany sometime early in May of 2006 and began a series of increasingly worrisome raids. Born in Italy to a Slovenian sow, he wandered the Italian countryside throughout his first two years of life before he, for reasons no one will ever know, pushed north into the thawing slopes and green valleys of the Austrian Alps. Western Austria is a narrow ribbon of land only fifty miles wide; to the north is Germany and to the south, Italy. In 2006, the bear left his Italian home and rambled through the narrow state of Tyrol, Austria, toward Germany, passing ski resorts and tiny farming hamlets. He crossed rivers, fording the waters of glacial melt as the first signs of spring came to the alpine villages. He ambled up and over the Ötztal Alps, passing through some of the most remote sections of Austria, where he was first sighted in the small village of Tösens in the Inntal Valley on May 5, 2006. His timing would prove a problem for Germany. The first World Cup team, the Togo national team, arrived in Germany on May 15 and began its preparations for the competition. Four days later, the bear, not even 100 miles away, made his first appearance in the country as well.

The village of Graswang, Germany, sits in the Ammergau range, a low set of mountains that makes up part of the outer rim of the Alps. A farming village, Graswang sees summer tourists, but those who visit are typically on their way to Linderhof Palace, a small mansion inspired by Versailles. Aside from a small church, there is little to see and little to do in Graswang. It is quiet, it is removed from traffic, and it is the perfect place for a bear to find easy prey.

The first sign of a bear in Germany occurred on May 19. South of Graswang, in a pasture flanked by limestone cliffs on one side and a small creek on another, a farmer found three of his sheep slain. The killings were striking, even to a farmer who had from time to time lost sheep to wild dogs that scavenge the valleys of Germany and Austria. He found two of the dead animals close to each other. Both had blood pouring from their necks, and both seemed to have been tossed in the air. Their legs were akimbo, and one of the sheep lay across the neck of the other. The way the two bodies were on top of each other suggested that the attack had been violent, which worried the farmer, but the third dead animal stopped him in his tracks. He found it in a grassy swale carved out of a low rise near the creek. It had been dismembered. Its throat had been ripped open, just like the others, and its shoulders bore vicious wounds, but a portion of its hindquarters was simply missing.

The farmer bent close to the animal, studying where the body had been clawed apart, noting a ragged tear just below the shoulders. Then he stood up and looked around the pasture. His eye caught a mound of white and red a dozen feet away. He walked toward it, looking around the field, curious but also a bit concerned. He wondered if the animal that had killed his sheep were still around. He wondered if he were alone in the field, and he listened for anything stirring in the brush and reeds bordering the creek.

When he finally came close enough to see the lower half of the animal, his mind focused on the horrific reality of the moment, and he knew that whatever had killed the sheep had to have been large. The rump and back legs of the creature had been rather neatly severed from the shoulders, neck, and head. Deep wounds punctured the haunches, and while a steady stream of red spilled from the cavity where the body had been torn in two, most of the wool on the remains was disturbingly white, as though the rear of the sheep had simply been popped cleanly from the rest of the animal, carried carefully to this particular spot, and left behind as some sort of exhibit. The farmer knew immediately that this was no ordinary mauling, and he called local authorities.

When police arrived, they declared it the work of feral dogs. The farmer, though, knew better. He guessed that something very different had attacked his flock, and he argued briefly with the local police about it. It could not be dogs, he said. Dogs do not tear animals in half, and if dogs had attacked the sheep, they would have eaten them. These sheep had not been eaten. They had been butchered and left behind. The official report, however, would not change: Dogs were the culprit. They had killed in the region before, and they had, according to official statements, simply done so again. No one there, however, could have guessed what had actually happened. They had no experience with the type of animal that could cause such impressive bloodshed, and they did not know that in Austria, a team of biologists had been following a bear that had already attacked more than a dozen animals.

In the middle of the next night, the bear made his second attack in Bavaria. Barely ten miles to the southeast of Graswang, near the town of Farchant, another farmer found slaughter. Two of his sheep had been tossed around their pen, their throats ripped out and ears chewed off. One was missing a foreleg, and the other had a gaping hole in its left hip where flesh had been torn from the bone. A lamb had also been killed and was virtually unrecognizable as an animal; it was simply a mass of gore and bone. Another sheep stood in the corner of the pen. When the farmer approached it, he realized that one of the animal's rear legs had been broken and that part of its face had been crushed by the force of a fearsome bite. The farmer killed the creature immediately to save it any further suffering.

Though separated by a mountain, these two small hamlets of Bavaria are closely connected communities, so the farmer had heard about the attacks in Graswang the night before. Neighbors share stories, pass on rumors, and generally look out for each other, so in Farchant, when the farmer found his mauled sheep, he knew that he had been a second victim to a strange attacker. He called the authorities.

The local police scoured the scene. One of the officers had been at Graswang and felt immediately that the attack looked the same as the one he had seen there. Both were unusual maulings, far different than those he occasionally encountered. At the Farchant site, however, he noticed something he had not seen at Graswang. Just outside the enclosure, a few feet from a wrecked fence, was a muddy path. In the mud, he found a track. It took him only a moment to recognize what had made it. A kind of primal recognition welled up inside of him, and part of him refused to believe what he saw. When he found a sample of coarse hair pinched in fence wire, he knew he would be able to confirm what his gut already told him. Even though he had never seen a bear track, and even though he had never held bear hair in his hands, he knew immediately what kind of animal he was now dealing with. He also knew that he had a big problem on his hands.

Bears were not supposed to be in Germany, and an aggressive bear at the height of the tourist season in Bavaria spelled disaster.

He immediately contacted regional biologists at government offices and the Bavarian State Ministry of the Environment and Consumer Protection. Ministry officials contacted Austrian officials, who confirmed that a bear had recently caused significant damage in Tyrol. Moreover, they told the Germans that they had listed the bear in Austria as "dangerous," an official classification that meant the bear was prone to attacking other animals and should be dealt with in an urgent manner. After talking to Bavarian officials and hearing about the events in Germany, however, the Austrian experts revised their classification of the bear. Because the animal appeared to be killing without restraint and because the killings were clearly not the result of hunger or predation, they re-listed the animal as "very dangerous." The new classification meant that the bear posed "an imminent threat to humans."

Germany responded quickly to the reclassification. Officials ordered the bear killed. Before anyone could be hurt or before the bear could threaten any more farmers' livestock and livelihoods, they would, on the evening of May 22, announce that hunters had free rein to track down and shoot the beast.

University of Vienna professor Felix Knauer, who was part of the Austrian assessment team and then a professor at University of Freiburg, went public with his opinion on the bear. He reviewed its history of attacks, describing in detail the animal's rampage across the Alps, and then expressed his support for the decision by the Bavarian ministry. The bear, he said, must be removed from the area. Austria had been patient in dealing with it, but now the time had come to act.

"We have underestimated," he said, "the danger posed by this bear."

Knauer could not have been more prophetic.

# 4

~~~

# A Bear Is Born

In 2004, deep in the Italian Alps, a brown bear was born. His name was JJ1, a name meaningful only to scientists who would track and monitor him throughout his life. This northern Italian bear, born of Slovenian parents, was among the first offspring of the Life Ursus campaign, and his birth was one of several widely lauded successes of the wildlife program. He was among the first generation of Italy's new northern brown bears.

His mother was one of the earliest Slovenian bears introduced into Italy. Her name was Jurka. She and four other bears from Slovenia had been trapped, situated into holding pens, then transported from their home to Adamello-Brenta Provincial Park in the Italian Alps. Though Slovenian by birth and upbringing, Jurka readily found a home in this idyllic land, and within a couple of years, she found a mate. Joze was another bear introduced from Slovenia, brought to Italy with a group of two others, Daniza and Irma, in an earlier wave of bears. Joze was a peaceful bear, as were Daniza and Irma, and though Daniza would make troubling headlines a decade later, Joze would remain best known as the peaceful father of JJ1.

Indeed, Joze seemed an especially suitable mate for Jurka because Jurka had developed some habits that local officials found concerning. Jurka, unfortunately, liked to visit villages.

And alpine huts.

And valley farms.

Frequently.

And when she visited, she liked to eat. A lot.

Jurka developed a reputation as a troublesome bear, a midnight raider whom locals came to distrust and dislike. She damaged livestock pens, ripped open cages, trashed garbage bins, and became an all-around nuisance.

Still, for all her meddling in the affairs of man, Jurka was nonetheless a skittish bear. She was quick to flee when confronted, and even the slightest suggestion that humans might be nearby sent her scrambling away. She was a troublesome bear, but she was not a dangerous bear. She posed no meaningful threat to people, at least at the time she rendezvoused with Joze. Maybe Joze could help tame Jurka just a bit. Or maybe Jurka's pairing with Joze suggested that she would abandon her less-than-desirable behaviors and return to being a "good bear."

How and where the two bears met will likely remain a mystery. If radio-collar GIS information documents it, it has not been made available. But, somewhere in the Dolomites during the 2003–2004 breeding season, Joze sauntered over to Jurka and began a courtship ritual. For brown bears, the ritual is not particularly elaborate. The male might follow the female for a few days, trailing her, sometimes hiding, sometimes within sight. When he finally approaches her, she often initially rejects him. She may even make a brusque "leave me alone" display by swatting at his nose.

Jurka at some point melted to the brazen *amore* of Joze's stalking and courting. She may have smacked his nose a couple of times, but eventually she warmed up and at some point, the two likely began nuzzling each other, rubbing their heads and necks against one another, maybe even rolling around a bit, tumbling in a meadow or along the forest floor. Brown bears sometimes even wrestle with each other, just to get into the mood. And so Jurka and Joze wrestled and nuzzled, and in the spring of 2004, Jurka gave birth to cubs, bears JJ1 and JJ2. Joze and Jurka were parents.

After mating, Jurka would almost immediately kick Joze to the curb—Joze would never know his cubs. Brown bears are raised solely by their mother, and indeed male bears have been known to attack and kill cubs. So Jurka would carry her cubs to term alone and then give birth to them in a safe place, far away from any intruders or witnesses. The cubs, often cradled as young, would bond with Jurka, hardly leaving her for the first few months of their lives.

At first, Jurka and her cubs behaved like normal bears. Researchers kept tabs on them, loosely accounting for their movements and activities. Jurka scavenged the high meadows and the forests for spring food, and the cubs nursed and thrived. They spent bright summer days rollicking, the cubs tumbling over each other in play and sunning themselves when their mother slept.

At some point before her cubs were one year old, though, Jurka returned to her old ways, sneaking into villages and onto farms to conduct raids for human riches. This time, though, she brought her cubs with her. And, like any young animals, the cubs learned quickly from their mother where to find the best food.

Brown bear cubs stay with their mothers for a little more than two years, and during that time, they grow stupendously fast. That growth requires significant energy, and while the mother's milk will sustain a cub for the first few weeks of life, bear cubs, by the time spring has moved into summer, require a wider diet. The mother is crucial at this time because she teaches the bears where to look for food. She flips over rocks and logs to reveal colonies of ants. She rips up plants to reveal edible roots. She tracks down berries and hunts for beehives hidden in trees or rock ledges. She models bear eating so the cubs learn what bears eat and where to find it.

Unfortunately, Jurka had hankerings for more than just ants. She had already developed a taste for honey in the wild, but she had also developed a taste for the easier-to-find honey of local farmers. Their apiaries provided no protection from the bears, so her raids on beehives helped teach her cubs that some meals are easier to get than others. All they needed to do was endure the sight, sounds, and smells of humans, and an almost limitless bounty could be theirs.

The cubs, undoubtedly, had little difficulty adapting. For animals first learning to track down meals, raiding trash cans, apiaries, and even small animal enclosures must have made life seem astonishingly rich and simple. Indeed, killing caged rabbits must have seemed entertaining as well as delicious, even if not as sporting as chasing wild ones. So by the time JJ1 and JJ2 left their mother in the spring of 2006, they had well established records as farm and village raiders. JJ1 in particular seemed to have a special knack for the activity. He had not only been sighted with Jurka in villages, but after Jurka had chased her cubs away to encourage them to go and live on their own, JJ1 took his mother's lessons with him and had been recorded breaking into compounds to secure a treat. Human settlement meant food. Delicious food. Endless and easy-to-acquire meals that JJ1 simply could not resist and that pointed to one simple truth about his upbringing: Jurka had trained him well.

# 5

*~~~*

# Petzi

In early spring of 2006, JJ1 headed north across the Dolomites, leaving his mother and brother behind in Italy and finding himself in a new country. Precisely when he left is a mystery, but sometime in late April or early May, he headed north and wandered into Austria.

The region between Italy and Austria where JJ1 traveled is rugged. Wide swaths of it are roadless, and high mountain peaks in the area climb to well over 10,000 feet. Villages are sparse, typically situated in the larger valleys. During World War I, Austrians and Italians fought the "White War" in these high mountains, and thousands succumbed to hypothermia and frostbite because they were so far from help. Many simply disappeared into the snow, and their remains have only recently been found, thanks to a warming climate and receding glaciers.

Today, long after wars raged in these mountains, the only significant source of revenue in the area is tourism, and while farms remain, they are typically small, family affairs with only local markets in mind. A brown bear traveling this area in early spring would likely come upon very few people. Ski season often extends into April, but 2006 was an especially warm winter and spring, legendary for its lack of snow. Snowfall was so light and the snowpack so thin that many slopes ended their seasons earlier than usual. If a bear wanted to travel undetected through northern Italy and into the Tyrol section of Austria, 2006 would have been the perfect year to do it. With not enough snow for skiers and too much melting and soft snow for hikers, the mountainsides were empty. JJ1 traveled in peace.

On May 5, however, in the tiny village of Tösens, someone saw him. In Tösens, a mecca for travelers seeking peace and quiet, the appearance of a bear was big news. JJ1 was, by then, a healthy young bear with a vibrant coat and strong chest and legs. His claws could be seen quite clearly from a distance. Austria already had a population of probably thirty brown bears, but they generally kept to the mountains and away from people. Many were in the eastern part of the country, far from the ranges where JJ1 now roamed, and in many cases, far from the more populated areas of Austria. JJ1, on the other hand, walked right up to the village edge, and at 10 p.m. on that warm early May night, a passerby noticed him and notified authorities.

JJ1 would not be seen again for eight days, but in that time, he would become well known in Austria. JJ1 began to haunt the valleys during the night, and he left behind disturbing signs of his visits. At first, he visited deer feeding stations. He tore his way into them, had a snack, and went on his way. But after a series of innocuous and predictable raids, his behavior changed significantly. Starting on May 9, he targeted livestock pens either within villages or right next to farm houses. Inside each pen, he left behind horrific carnage.

On the first night, he mauled eleven sheep in a village called Gargellen, just over the mountains but in another province than Tösens. One of the sheep was gored and died immediately, and two others would later be euthanized because their injuries were so extensive. Deep gashes across their backs bled dark red, and torn ears dangled like the broken wings of a butterfly. The remaining sheep, terrified and wounded, would be treated by their owner and by veterinarians. The next night in another town, JJ1 killed a ram before he traveled to another area, where he broke down the door to an outbuilding to enter a pigsty. There, he thrashed around and left large and well-defined prints. A night later, he tore into silage bales and another deer feeding station.

By the time a group of hunters saw JJ1 at 6 a.m. on May 13, he had mauled more than a dozen animals. One of his quarry would not be found for another day, and, at the time, was misidentified as killed by a dog. Concerningly, most of the mauled animals were simply killed and left behind—the bear did not eat them. Indeed, the attacks seemed to suggest that JJ1 was utterly unconcerned with feeding. He appeared to be killing for sport, but, more alarmingly, he was doing so in the heart of villages, willing to break down doors to gain access to his victims.

The degree and nature of the damage concerned local officials, and they convened a group of experts to address the matter. The Austrian Bear Emergency Team was the brainchild of Felix Knauer. In the 1990s, Knauer recognized the need to have a group of experts ready to intervene on behalf of the bears in case there were conflicts between the animals and humans. The group initially consisted of just him and another colleague, but it grew to include a cadre of volunteers and scientists. He founded the group while he was working in Austria alongside the World Wildlife Fund, which had helped oversee a reintroduction of brown bears into the Austrian Alps. He had in previous years developed a knack for trapping bears, something he intentionally curated as one of his skill sets while working on research projects in Croatia and in northern Italy in 1991.

As a child, Knauer had spent endless hours in the forests. He wandered the woods day and night, learning the sights and sounds of woodland. He jokes today that while his friends were out learning about girls, he was learning about wildlife.

As a young man, he came under the tutelage of an old hunter who showed him how to stalk and anticipate prey. By the time he reached adulthood, Knauer had probably spent more time outdoors than indoors, and he used the skills he had developed under the old man to transform himself from hunter to trapper.

His ability to track, identify, and trap bears was surprising. He speaks about it matter-of-factly, in the same way that a chef might say, "Yes, I can cook some pasta." The understated truth is that he has a reputation second to none for locating and securing bears, especially problem bears. When he witnessed the ongoing reintroduction of bears into western Europe, he instinctively knew that it would bring with it greater opportunity for human contact with the animals. More important, he knew this would lead to calls to destroy bears. He was right, and he provided an alternative to killing animals. The Bear Emergency Team anticipated the need to solve the issue of "problem bears" and established a trapping and deterrence protocol. The group developed, together with stakeholders and authorities, an action plan that could be generalized and used by localities throughout Europe, a kind of "best practices" for bear-human coexistence, and the organization lobbied to put it in place in the event of problematic encounters between bears and humans. It was a prescient move. Throughout the 1990s, the team was repeatedly called to help with "problem bears," and from 1995 to 1998, at the pinnacle of the bear recovery in Austria, the team trapped and moved six bears. The arrival of JJ1 a decade later, however, would be its greatest test.

Knauer slowly withdrew from the daily work of the response team in the late 1990s. He had decided to pursue his academic work, and, with limited time, handed over the reins to others. He continued to consult with them, but when JJ1 arrived in Austria, he was busy with his work at the University of Freiburg. During his time with the response team, he had helped many towns cope with bear issues, but JJ1 appeared to be different, and when he and his colleagues saw the mounting problems the bear was creating, they knew they would need all available experience. They, Knauer now acknowledges, underestimated this particular bear emergency. Or, perhaps more precisely, they were ill-equipped to handle the spectacle and public pressure that accompanied JJ1.

At the time, no one knew for sure where JJ1 had come from. Was he an Italian bear, or was he an Austrian bear? Could he possibly be some other bear altogether? Many officials guessed it may be one of Jurka's cubs. Both of them, when young, had displayed the kind of unpredictable village intrusions that officials were witnessing in Austria, and both had been essentially AWOL since their mother chased them from her own territory. The consensus among most officials was that the bear was JJ2, Jurka's younger cub. JJ2 had been in trouble more recently in Italy, and the raids seemed in keeping with his activity.

Yet a DNA sample taken from scat and hair on May 15, 2006, refuted the possibility that it was JJ2, so the emergency response team began work under the assumption that it was either JJ1 or an unknown bear. The tests also confirmed, however, that the bear was not an Austrian bear, causing some of the group to breathe sighs of relief. Concern had lingered that the bear was one of the established Austrian population. That group had been remarkably quiet in recent years, and while its virtual invisibility to the local farmers and the press had meant that the bears had been able to breed and grow unmolested by humans, it also meant that researchers and team members were not exactly sure where they all were or what they all were doing. So when the DNA tests confirmed that the lineage was clearly from the Slovenian reintroduction in northern Italy, the response team felt relief as much as anything. Despite the mystery of the bear's identity, at least one concrete piece of information was clear: He was an Italian bear descended from the Slovenian Life Ursus campaign.

The same morning the team received the first DNA test results, a couple who owned a high alpine hut snapped the first picture of the bear.

While not particularly helpful in identifying the bear, the photo for the first time provided clear evidence of the size and health of the animal. The photograph also confirmed that the bear seemed unconcerned with humans. It came within only a few feet of the hut, and the husband and wife, on the hut's porch, snapped photos of it as it walked by. The bear would have known they were there. The proximity, paired with the smells and the snapping of the camera shutter, would have made the bear aware that he was near humans. Yet he did not run away, nor did he seem in any particular hurry. He simply went about his business, unconcerned about the man and woman so close to him.

The encounter raised red flags for the emergency response team. A "good bear" does not ignore people it knows are nearby. It flees them. It may show signs of curiosity, or it may initially approach to just inquire a bit about what it is seeing or smelling, but, in general, a brown bear avoids humans as surely as humans avoid it. Despite occasional bear attacks on humans, the fact is that the vast majority of them want nothing to do with us. They flee at first sign, and since the bears' sense of smell is so well developed, odds are they flee long before we have a chance to see them.

The Bear Emergency Team invoked its system of bear management and gave the bear a label that would likely spell its doom. Knauer's group had years ago developed a system of designations that could help local governments decide which bears posed problems and which ones did not. The system relied on field reports of animal behavior. Certain behaviors in isolation likely meant that the bear was just behaving normally. One bear who lived in Austria for more than twenty years was like this. Quiet and reclusive, he hardly ever approached human settlements. Every once in a while, though, he would raid a farmer's beehive for some honey. The infrequency of the occurrences and the fact that the bear habitually avoided people meant the bear was a "good bear." In terms of Knauer's system, this was a "normal and natural" bear, and no action was needed.

The next level up was a "critical" bear situation, which requires some action but without urgency. There is no need to call in the SWAT team, but the animal needs to be addressed and reconditioned. The next level up is a "dangerous" bear. This bear requires immediate action. In most cases, that means a series of behavior deterrence actions, things like pelting the bear with rubber bullets or waiting for the bear to return to a raided site and then startling it with loud noises or physical deterrents. But, if the bear is immune to deterrence, the plan calls for removal of the bear by trapping or tranquilizing. The final stage of Knauer's system labels the bear a "very dangerous" bear. This bear, depending on the severity of its behaviors, might be a target for removal by trapping, but in other cases, the bear must be, according to this category, terminated. It poses too great of a threat to humans.

Besides providing categories with which to assess a bear, Knauer's system aims for more nuance by also identifying individual bear acts within the established hierarchy. So a bear might be labeled "critical," but certain of its behaviors could be deemed—again according to the system the emergency team uses—"dangerous." The labeling of incidents in addition to overall behavior allows the team to assess not only the larger situation but the potential escalation or de-escalation of a bear's individual acts. It allows the team to ask more nuanced questions about the bear's behavior and to recommend more measured and thoughtful responses to the bear in question.

Knauer's team, which was working on the assumption that the bear was JJ1, labeled him a "dangerous" bear in need of immediate response. At a press conference, officials announced plans to trap and radio-collar the bear. The purpose of the radio collar would be primarily to track the bear, but it would also help officials anticipate its behavior so that deterrents could be planned for any future conflict with the local community.

The press conference marked the first public discussion of JJ1, but it would not be the last. In a little over a week, the bear left Austria and became the first wild bear to step onto German soil in 150 years. He would never know the chaos he was about to cause or understand the celebrity he was about to achieve, but he would become the most famous bear the world had ever known. As such, the press rushed to name him.

Local media started calling him "Petzi," a bear from a Danish children's book series and comic strip. Petzi was a friendly bear whose adventures, illustrated for children and even developed into a play, made for lighthearted and endearing reading; the images of Petzi are joyful and innocent. The bear who traveled from Italy through Austria and into Bavaria, though—the one slaughtering helpless sheep and brazenly entering homesteads to seek out animals to maul—hardly matched with the image of Petzi. So despite even *Der Spiegel* using the name, "Petzi" never took hold.

Another name did, though. Less than a week after calling him Petzi, *Der Spiegel* called him by a new name, and in the coming months, the newspaper would launch a column dedicated to reports of the bear's antics and atrocities. "Bruno Watch" would eventually become the newspaper's most popular column of the year, and, for much of the summer of 2006, its namesake would make headlines around the globe.

Bruno the bear was born.

# 6

~~~

# Bruno Attacks

Bruno did not stay in Germany after he first crossed into the country. At least, not at first. Instead, he wandered back into the Austrian Alps, but not until he had left behind a trail of such gore that even some local papers refused to print photographs of the bear's assaults.

From May 19 to May 22, Bruno raided at least four farms and killed eleven sheep and almost a dozen birds, both chicken and dove. Farmers and shepherds were now well aware of the dangers of the bear, and they had begun notifying each other of any possible sightings. In beer halls and in mountain huts, Bruno was the primary topic of conversation, most of it fixated on the damage he was doing. Any initial sense that the bear might be a welcome addition to the Bavarian mountains rapidly evaporated. Locals wanted Bruno dead. The sooner the better.

The problem was that locals were not the only ones interested in Bruno's life. Bear enthusiasts suddenly appeared across Europe. Nurtured by media coverage of Bruno's travels, widespread fascination with the animal grew rapidly into unprecedented celebrity. One British financier even offered $2 million to help aid the efforts to protect Bruno. More important, in 2006, masses of soccer fans descending on Germany wanted him to stay to greet them. Bruno enjoyed wide support, and the public's wishes could not be ignored.

Plans for how to deal with Bruno started as private deliberations between conservationists and government officials, but as media coverage of the animal slaughters grew, the local population demanded to know the plan. They wanted the bear gone, and they wanted clear evidence that officials had the situation under control. Of course, the situation was anything but under control, but at the time, officials believed they had Bruno in the crosshairs, and they held news conferences to convey their plan to the public. Their first plan was simple: They would trap Bruno and then convey him to an enclosure many miles away. There, he would spend the rest of his days trotting about a three-square-mile enclosure, limited in his range but not entirely domesticated.

The response to the plan was mixed but trending toward positive. The locals could be assured the bear was removed, and environmentalists could be assured the bear would not be harmed. Soccer fans could enjoy the spectacle of a trapped bear even as they could root him on in his new life as a transplant to Germany. It seemed as close to a win-win plan as anyone could offer.

The first attempt to capture Bruno occurred near one of his more ruthless killings. Bruno had found his way into a fold in a tiny vale called Reschberg. Reschberg is not visible on maps of the area, but the nearby town of Farchant is, and there, news of Bruno's attacks on May 20 led to both terror and outrage.

Farchant is a quiet village not twenty miles from the Austrian border. Other than small farms, local hotels and hostels comprise the primary industry, and hikers and bikers often use the town as a home base. That May, Bruno made his way into a small herd of sheep and systematically gored four of the animals. Two of the adults had their throats ripped out, and a lamb was bitten across the back, its spine crushed, and its lung collapsed. A second lamb succumbed to its wounds the next day, and the shepherd, furious, declared through tears that the bear attack had terrified his entire flock. "You don't know what it's like to see the fear in their eyes," he said in an interview with the BBC.

That night, the Bear Emergency Team set its first trap in a culvert not far from the killings. Hunks of flesh from the dead sheep were used as bait, with the hope that Bruno would return to feast on his dead. He did not. Indeed, he rarely did. Throughout his journeys in Bavaria, he almost never returned to the site of his crimes. He simply killed and left. And for people like Felix Knauer, that was a bad sign.

After two nights of failed trappings, the Bavarian State Ministry of the Environment and Consumer Protection convened a meeting with the Bear Emergency Team and local officials. The bear team announced that, by their assessment, the bear had now moved up on their rating scale from "dangerous" to "very dangerous." As such, they argued, he presented an imminent threat to people, and more resources were needed to neutralize him.

The Bavarian ministry took the escalation as license to do what many within the government had wanted to do in the first place. So they made a decision. Hunters were free to kill Bruno.

Knauer, continuing to advocate in his position on the Bear Emergency Team, did not want Bruno dead. He still believed the bear could be caught. Certainly, he held no illusions about the bear. He knew Bruno was dangerous, and he feared he would eventually harm a person if he was not stopped. But Knauer believed Bruno could still be caught and relocated, and he believed that doing so was a reasonable course of action, even if hunters would pursue him at the same time.

So, despite orders from the Bavarian ministry, the bear team continued with its attempts to capture Bruno by setting up traps in culverts where he was likely to travel. Simultaneously, the ministry granted licenses to local hunters to shoot the bear. By doing so, the ministry effectively hedged its bets. The people most worried about living with the animal in their backyard had the right to kill it, but experts had the opportunity to protect it. Who knew? Maybe the hunters would scare it into one of the traps. Either way, the bear would be gone, and the problem would be solved. Either way, the ministry had a win.

The ministry could not have been more wrong. As a regional governmental body tasked with very specific mandates concerning land management, the ministry could not have anticipated the backlash to its kill order. Officials felt they had done their due diligence and, more important, were working alongside both experts and local constituents. They had checked all the environmental and governmental boxes, and had gone beyond any reasonable measure to work to preserve the bear. So they had reason to expect that their order, which still allowed for trapping even as it also allowed locals to put an end to the menace if they had a chance, would be largely embraced, even if disagreed upon by some activist groups.

They were probably right that in most instances, their order to kill a bear would likely have been a minor issue that, even if controversial, would have hardly made an impact on the region. If anyone outside of Bavaria cared, they would have been radical voices from the edge, and few in Germany tolerated such voices. But the ministry could not fully account for what made 2006 so different from any other time. A few months earlier, their kill order would not have mattered. A few months later, the same. But in May of 2006, media from around the globe were in Germany sniffing around for stories, and a German hit on an endangered animal seemed like a perfect way to fill columns and newswires.

Among the first of the international media to cover Bruno was the *Los Angeles Times*, which ran a feature on Bruno on May 26, shortly after the hit had been ordered. "Grin and Bear It? No Way, Germans Say" read the headline. The story detailed Bruno's misadventures in Austria and Germany, contrasting the anger about the bear in Germany with Austrian acceptance of the animal as one of their own. "People in the two countries," the article reads, "appear to be making increasingly wild assertions. Some Austrians are claiming the bear is under the protection of Pope Benedict XVI, who, they say, recently has added a bear to his crest. Germans contend that the bear is 'out of control.'"

A few days earlier, the UK's *Guardian* and *Independent* both ran stories noting German frustration with the bear. The Italian press, feeling a kinship with their prodigal son, was less diplomatic. *La Repubblica* ran a feature with the headline, "In Bavaria, the Bear Has Returned after 170 Years, But the Germans Want to Kill Him." Canada's *Globe and Mail* ran a feature within the week titled "Visitor Becomes Unbearable," a pun that did little to allay concerns of conservationists.

These headlines were just the beginning. The Bruno story caught fire, and within a day of the officials' issuing the kill order, backlash was so pervasive and intense that they were forced to withdraw it. Bruno, they assured the public, would be given a fair chance to be caught and relocated. They would use the finest trackers and the best technology to find, trap, and move him to a place where he could not do any harm. The masses celebrated, and *Der Spiegel* praised the attempts to spare the animal and honor a new, modern attitude among Germans about conservation and wild animals.

Bruno's stay of execution, of course, only heightened public interest in him. Here was an animal who had escaped the hand of German justice and who ambled along blithely unaware of the drama he was creating. By the end of May, news readers and viewers sought out Bruno stories with astonishing fervor. They logged onto the Internet to learn about his latest antics, and they sought as much information as they could about his location. Some even traveled to Bavaria to track him down, while others watched from a distance, hoping that someone would snap a clear picture of him. His celebrity grew to such a degree that international reporters seemed far more interested in him than in Germany's notorious soccer mania. The bear was beginning to overshadow the biggest sporting event in the world, and German officials were not amused.

# 7

~~

# The Hunt for Bruno

On May 29, 2006, Bruno the bear was positively identified as JJ1. Now, there was no longer any doubt which bear Germans were confronting and worldwide media were valorizing.

After Germany revoked the kill order, debates around how best to capture the bear began to swell. Knauer and the Bear Emergency Team continued to set traps in culverts near bear killings. On the morning the bear was identified, a taxi driver saw Bruno cross the road in front of him, and team members were sent to investigate. Much of the activity was located in Austria, but German officials kept a close eye on the developments, not convinced that their confrontation with Bruno was over.

Still, from May 23 to June 3, most bear sightings and tracking activity occurred in the Tyrol region of Austria. A team of bear and large-mammal specialists from an organization called *Vier Pfoten*, or Four Paws, based out of Austria, descended on the area and implemented a new tactic to lure and trap the bear—a nightmarish method, it seemed like something from the Middle Ages. First, they gathered the stomachs of slaughtered cows, deer, pigs, or sheep and tied them to the end of ropes. The flesh surrounding the stomach remained attached to the organ, and blood still ran fresh from it.

They then tied the other ends of the ropes to vehicles and drove them along roads where they suspected the bear might roam. Slick lines of flesh and blood streaked across the asphalt and baked in the early summer heat. The gruesome "scent lines" were intended to lure Bruno into the open, but after two and a half days of grizzly baiting, Four Paws abandoned the project. On June 1, the organization announced it would follow other protocols and the wishes of Tyrolian officials in their efforts to find and neutralize the bear.

For nearly ten days, Bruno was virtually invisible. Occasional bear prints surfaced in various locations, and signs of bear scavenging appeared in both valleys and mountain passes. Occasionally, someone called in a sighting to the police, and both media and officials swarmed to investigate. Bruno was never seen. In one instance, an alarmed homeowner called officials because she found a bear print on her window, but close investigation revealed that it was actually the handprint of a family member who had been working at the windowsill.

Bruno's ghost lingered over the region. Phantom sightings became an almost hourly occurrence, testing the patience of police and volunteers. Few reports amounted to anything, and telling fact from fiction became increasingly difficult. Officials spent as much time chasing down rumors as they did tracking Bruno himself.

But when three viciously mauled sheep were discovered in Bavaria on the morning of June 4, Germans knew instantly that Bruno had emerged from his time in the shadows. Near the village of Klais, a group of tourists traveling by car spotted bloody masses in a pasture. The three sheep, their throats ripped from their bodies, were spread across a verdant Bavarian hillside. When the landowner and officials arrived to inspect the kills, they found other casualties. Three more sheep and a goat had also been mauled, one of the sheep and the goat so badly injured that the owner immediately killed them in an act of mercy.

The very next night, Bruno struck again, this time in a place so beautiful that the carnage seemed to mock the landscape. Right at the edge of an alpine lake near the village of Mittenwald, a popular tourist spot with its lakefront restaurants and recreation activities, Bruno killed a sheep.

The timing was fortunate: Any later in the summer, and Bruno's attack would have been in full view of anyone sitting on restaurant decks overlooking the lake. More concerning, however, was the fact that Bruno also chased down a sheep and two rams that initially escaped him. Ducking wire fences, the terrified animals bolted for the lake and ran directly into a courtyard next to a children's playground. Within a hundred feet of the buildings, Bruno caught the female, ripping open her belly and biting deep into her neck. He then pursued the rams directly into a settlement along the lake. The rams scattered, ultimately escaping his jaws, but Bruno left a sign of his visit. Not five feet from a food and beverage kiosk where children line up in the summer to buy ice cream, a giant paw print was sunk deep into the mud. An image of it, startling in its proximity to human activity, hit the papers and led to even more intense press coverage.

While the Bear Emergency Team had already labeled Bruno an imminent threat to people, the maulings near Mittenwald only confirmed their worries and bred more urgency among all the groups trying to corral him. Everyone knew that if Bruno were not trapped soon, he would confront either a hapless sightseer who would be ill-prepared to defend himself or a disgruntled local farmer ready to take matters into his own hands. Neither scenario would end well.

Knauer's team worked behind the scenes to try to placate German officials who were growing impatient with attempts to trap Bruno. Bavarian ministers were fielding daily inquiries about the status of Bruno and their attempts to capture and relocate him and enduring increasing pressure from national officials to get Bruno under control. Media fascination with the bear had overwhelmed coverage of the

World Cup, for which Germany had been preparing for more than a decade and on which more than a few people had pinned their professional aspirations. The bear was not simply a distraction for them, but a genuine threat to the success of rebuilding Germany's international reputation as a progressive state. A lumbering animal disrupting daily life was more than some of them could tolerate. They wanted the bear gone. Quickly.

From late May and through June, the best-selling German tabloid *TZ* ran so many cover stories on Bruno—eleven front-page stories in less than a month, more than they had dedicated to any person or event in such a short time over the previous decade—that public pressure on officials to spare the animal's life dwarfed all other public mandates. *Der Spiegel*, much more highly regarded than *TZ*, was not immune to Bruno's story, and their "Bruno Watch" column likely did more to turn the tide against official calls for Bruno's killing than any other source. It also did as much damage to Germany's reputation for efficiency and ingenuity because it delighted in relating tales of official misadventure or incompetence in handling the bear. "Bruno Watch" and the tabloids were as obsessed with official miscues as they were with Bruno himself. Local bungling made for especially savory stories.

On more than one occasion in early June, local police in Bavaria dismissed reports of bear sightings or bear attacks as flights of the imagination, only to learn that Bruno had, in fact, appeared. On the night of June 5, Bruno snatched two rabbits from a hutch. One he bit in half, and the other he must have devoured whole; it was never found. When the owner reported the event to police, they dismissed it as a cruel joke by a neighbor, but a follow-up by bear investigators uncovered bear hairs from the rabbit cage. The hutch was located between two apartment buildings, so though the death of rabbits in itself was not particularly worrying, its location, within feet of two multi-unit buildings, suggested that Bruno had no fear of being near human habitation.

The following night, in the wee hours of the morning, two twenty-somethings decided to scour the countryside to see if they could stumble upon the bear. At 3 a.m., against all odds, they located him on a road in Tyrol, barely five miles from the German border. They reported their sighting to the police, who immediately dismissed it as a prank, but when investigators followed up, they found Bruno's tracks in the mud in the precise location of the sighting.

Of course, police and naturalists were sorting through an almost endless parade of false identifications and outright deceit, so their dismissal of some reports makes sense. Hikers would send in photos of bear tracks only to learn that they had photographed dog prints. A jogger claimed to have watched Bruno attack a wild hare simply for sport, killing it and then leaving the body behind. She collected the remains, but no evidence of the bear on the remains or in the area was found to corroborate her story. Pranksters called in false reports, resulting in waste of police manpower and increasing skepticism of any story. All the while, Bruno continued his journey across the Alps and left destruction in his wake.

After his killing spree in early June, Bruno again disappeared. Brief sightings helped officials track his general whereabouts, but they remained frustrated with Bruno's evasiveness. Local farmers and shepherds became impatient, and on June 8, a faction of them declared that they had had enough. They would, as the official bear report would later read, "take the bear capture into their own hands." They devised a plan whereby they would work with local hunters to establish an alert system. When the bear was sighted, they would contact others in the system, including a veterinarian who was part of the provincial government. Immediately upon notification, the veterinarian would fly by helicopter to the bear's location and help the hunters tranquilize the animal.

The local activism resulted in almost immediate counteraction by the German and Austrian governments. In a move that some believed to be simply a publicity stunt to regain control of the story of Bruno, provincial authorities agreed to retain the services of a supposedly elite group of Finnish bear hunters. The Finnish Emergency Bear Team comprised highly specialized hunters who used Norwegian Elkhounds to track and capture problem bears. Elkhounds are a special breed of dog renowned for their ability to track, and in Finland, they had been bred to isolate bears and lead their owners to them. The Finns were, essentially, the special forces of bear hunting, and officials hoped that retaining them would bring an end to Bruno's adventures. They hoped as well that they would bring an end to the circus that was distracting from Germany's more important successes.

It was June 9, 2006, the night of the opening ceremonies of Germany's World Cup, yet June 9 marked not only the first night of the Cup; it also marked the night that Germany would finally call in the cavalry to put an end to the distraction that was Bruno the bear.

The Finns—and their dogs—were coming.

# 8

~~~

# Taunt

On June 11, 2006, the Finnish bear team began its work. The team had flown into Munich the day before, the first day of game play of the World Cup, and had been transported to Innsbruck, where members met with officials and began preparations for their hunt. They brought with them five Norwegian Elkhounds. Though called "elk" dogs, the breed hunt moose. In Scandinavian languages, the word for moose is *elk* or *elg,* and elk, as English-speaking countries know them, have different names, such as *hirvi,* in Finnish. The Elkhound's self-confidence is legendary.

When the Finnish team began its work in Bavaria and Austria, it did so secretly for the first day and half. Team members wanted the dogs to get adjusted to their surroundings, and they wanted to avoid the fanfare that accompanied Bruno. On June 12, however, officials held a press conference outdoors on a sunny green to introduce the team and its dogs to the world. Press from more than twenty countries attended, and headlines promptly followed in Europe and abroad.

Inside Germany, however, the press continued to mock its own officials. *Der Spiegel* ran a column the day that the Finns were trotted out that essentially ignored their arrival. "'Problem Bear' Strikes Again," read the headline, and the opening lines of the story bounced between serious and mocking tones, pointing out that Bruno had killed animals from flocks of sheep to single rabbits without even eating them, and ominously took note of his wide and alarming trail of destruction.

The article noted the ongoing frustration of German officials in trying to stop Bruno's "problem" killings, but then added a gem of a critique leveled by the Austrian chancellor: "[A]ll I have to say is this: If Europe has nothing else to worry about other than Bruno the bear, then it must be a happy place."

The newspaper ratcheted up the critique the next day. Though Bruno had been quiet overnight, the Finnish bear team suffered its first setback, and there would be many in the following days. Just after a World Cup report on Brazil's first win of the tournament —"Brazil Delivers Tepid 1-0 Win Over Strong Croatia"—*Der Spiegel*'s "Bruno Watch" column delivered a mocking headline that ridiculed the Finnish bear team. They used the language of the World Cup to make their point: "1-0 for Bavarian Bear as Finnish Hunting Dogs Can't Take Heat." The famously resilient Norwegian Elkhounds had crumbled under a sweltering and dry summer sun. Their breeding, it turns out, was made for the cooler climes of Scandinavia, and an early summer heat wave paired with the unusual amount of travel left the animals exhausted and unable to continue after only a couple of hours of searching.

The following day, other problems presented themselves. While the dogs had hunted in all sorts of forbidding wilderness terrain in the far north, they had not experienced the thin air of the Alps, nor had they been used to the elevation climbs and drops that constitute a mountain hunt. Bruno, loping around the region, carried his huge body up and down the mountains with ease, and in one notable moment, the dogs tracked the bear to a scree fall that was so steep and so pitched that the dogs simply sat on their haunches and looked up. Their handlers did much the same. Bruno, though, had simply leapt to the top of it, leaving his pursuers behind. No one could believe the bear made it over the rocky ridge, but he had with such ease and effortlessness that the Finnish bear team was left wondering how, if at all, it was ever going to corner the animal.

In the days that followed, Bruno sightings increased significantly. His proximity to humans resulted in more and more encounters, and the flood of tourists into the country only heightened the possibility of direct contact. A day after *Der Spiegel*'s mocking "1-0" headline, three separate groups of people saw Bruno in Bavaria, and the Finnish team was scrambled to locate the bear. Each of the dogs was equipped with a radio collar so that it could pursue its game freely. At one of the sites, a dog immediately picked up Bruno's trail and dashed into the woods. The team then followed at a distance until the dog settled into one spot and began barking.

Bruno, however, seemed immune to such sophisticated attempts to control him. Only 100 meters from where the dog had disappeared into the woods, Bruno reappeared, having apparently circled back, initially leading the dog in the wrong direction before backtracking. Bruno climbed up and over a culvert and onto a road, escaping for a moment.

After evading capture by dog, though, Bruno collided with a speeding car on a roadway. At 11 p.m., a vehicle struck him. A motorcyclist approaching the scene saw Bruno scuttle away, apparently unharmed, and rumble down a hillside toward a small reservoir. The car's mirror had only glanced him, and the owner of the car stopped and investigated. He rightly claimed to have been the only person to get within a foot of the beast. The dogs and their owners had no such luck.

The misadventures of the expert bear-hunting team from Finland rapidly became a running joke in the German media and remained so for years; even a play was written about it, featuring bumbling hunters and slapstick humor to represent the folly of the entire

Finnish dog venture. Bruno himself, in the play and in the media, came to stand for poor planning and poor policy, both anathema to Germans. Throughout early June of 2006, Bruno appeared time and again in news stories as a blend of a rebel and a saint who exposes gaps in German wildlife management and environmental policy. The emerging impact of new media forms only escalated his status as cultural icon. The burgeoning world of blogging and the expansion of Internet gaming ushered in Bruno's celebrity. That year, the most popular online game in Europe, "Hunt Bruno," was based on Germany's failed attempts to catch the bear. Bruno, the escape artist, became a hero.

And a teddy bear. More than one entrepreneurial sort peddled Bruno stuffed animals. With the country full of tourists, a better time could not be imagined for marketing a cuddly toy of a famous bear. Bears began to supplant the official mascots of the World Cup: Goleo, a lion, and Pille, a somewhat creepy talking soccer ball. One outfit even sold a high-end snuggly for more than $150 a pop.

Bear experts, however, did not see much teddy bear in Bruno. They were, in fact, becoming increasingly alarmed at the bear's behavior. Though they had not found any savage kills since the Finns had hit the ground, the bear was getting closer and closer to people. He had demonstrated since his youth that he was not afraid to go near buildings or into enclosures. He had been trained to do so by his mom, Jurka. But now, he seemed willing to approach people's living places in broad daylight, entirely unconcerned by their presence. Over a period of three days, he suddenly started getting even closer to people themselves, not just their homes, ultimately coming within forty feet of one farmer and walking across the terrace of a local lodge. The *New York Times* declared that "Herr Bruno Is Having a Picnic, But He Is No Teddy Bear," noting that at the time of the article's printing, Bruno had killed at least thirty animals, most of whom he had not bothered to eat. He had just slayed them and moved on.

Knauer and his Bear Emergency Team knew time and tolerance for Bruno were growing thin. While they had argued initially that the government should spare the bear's life, they knew that the increasing number of human encounters posed a real threat to human safety. No one was suggesting that Bruno was going to stalk and kill a person, but Knauer and his colleagues knew that an accidental encounter on a hiking trail or an unexpected confrontation in a livestock fold was only a matter of time, given his behavior. They would need to capture him quickly, or they would not have a chance to save him.

Their timeline accelerated even more on the night of June 17. At half past midnight, a man, cigarette in hand, stepped onto the balcony of a café after a night of eating, drinking, and visiting with friends. From there, to his utter shock, he saw the bear across the road, right in the heart of Kochel am See, a lakeside resort town. The beast lumbered into the open from an alley between buildings, milled about for a moment, then sniffed the air, surveying his surroundings with about as much concern as the town drunk. He took a couple more steps, plopped down on some stairs leading up into a traditional whitewashed building, then scratched himself while enjoying the view across the square.

Above him, a steeple rose from the roof, and the scene must have looked like something out of a movie: a large brown bear lounging on the front steps of a bright white Bavarian steeplehouse in the darkness of a June night. A couple of others in the café came out when the man started yelling, "The bear! The bear!" and the small group watched as Bruno loitered for a moment before ambling off into the night.

The scene would have been remarkable under any circumstances, but because Bruno had gotten a reputation for making fools of those who would trap him, it was a particularly brazen action. Even though he would have no way of knowing, Bruno had just mocked local authorities to such a degree that he had effectively sealed his fate.

The white building on whose steps he had lounged was, in fact, the police station. He had walked right up to the police department's front entry and, in an unparalleled display of bravado, lounged on its steps.

Bruno's taunt would not go unnoticed.

The next morning, the UK's *Guardian* ran a story that summed up the result of his actions. "Heat Turned Up on Bruno Bear," the headline read. The article cited Bruno's actions later the previous night at Kochel am See, noting that after he left the police station, he killed a rabbit and a guinea pig, then raided a local apiary, destroying a hive. The report also noted that the Bavarian environmental minister was no longer amused with the animal's antics. The minister issued a statement that was picked up by the UPI newswire and even NBC News in the US. Though Bruno had not physically harmed anybody, he had done something much, much worse.

He had made a fool of those who had already lost all patience with him.

The ministry made its decision. It was time to kill Bruno.

# 9

## Bruno, Enemy of the State

On June 30, 2006, United States diplomats in Germany sent a cable to State Department headquarters about Bruno the bear. Pointing to Kochel am See as a turning point for how Germans handled the beast, it summarized the country's final plan for Bruno: The Bavarian government declared Bruno "Ursus non Grata" and ordered that he be shot or captured. Vexed by Bruno's unchecked roaming across Bavaria, Minister-President Edmund Stoiber took to referring to him as "the Problem Bear."

The "problem bear" was winning a public relations war and distracting Germany from its other major event, the World Cup. Bruno, the cable continued, "appeared to win the battle for the hearts and minds of the public." The phrasing was pointed and would have resonated with department officials. Bruno presented an opportunity to review how a figure who ravaged an area could still win local support. No matter how many times German officials labeled him a problem or described his violence, the German public and the tourists in the country overwhelmingly wanted the bear captured and preserved. Indeed, the more German officials described his activities, the more the public seemed to want him to escape. He had become legendary precisely because he could not be contained and would not submit to official plans.

Within only a couple of days of Bruno's time in Kochel am See, the Bavarian State Ministry of the Environment and Consumer Protection called a meeting to discuss and reassess the capture strategy. While officials retained in principle a plan to capture and relocate the bear, the tenor of the meeting suggested that Bruno's time had run out. Bruno continued to kill more sheep, chickens, and rabbits; a day after the meeting, Bruno even approached a group of people at an alpine cabin, coming within fifty feet of them in the early morning. The next day at five in the morning, another group of people, this time in a car, witnessed Bruno chasing down, killing, and feeding on a sheep. They attempted to scare him off by honking their horn at him, but he was unconcerned, which was particularly unsettling for many of the people trying to capture him.

That same day, the Finnish bear team called it quits. It was late June, and they had been on Bruno's trail for eleven days. Their dogs were exhausted. The bear was elusive in ways they had never encountered before, but they also no longer had the full support of Bavarian officials. It was clear to most of them that the plan to capture Bruno had come to an end. Less than twenty-four hours later, Knauer and his Bear Emergency Team followed suit and disbanded.

Knauer was clear-eyed about the situation. He knew Bruno had been testing too many limits and that, eventually, if they could not capture him, the German officials would feel they had to end the threat. Indeed, he felt a confrontation between the bear and a human was inevitable if Bruno was not captured. Though the bear had conducted most of his raids deep in the night, over the past couple of days, he had apparently grown comfortable with daytime jaunts into human habitat. The early morning approach to the cabin, when paired with Bruno's killing of the sheep while the car honked at him, suggested that he simply no longer feared people. With so many tourists in the country and so many people actually daring to try to catch a glimpse of him, human contact was inevitable and, Knauer worried, inevitably tragic.

The decision to disband his team came as much from the realization that their tactics to capture Bruno were not working as it did from any lack of confidence expressed by the Bavarian ministry, but this did not make the decision any easier. Nor did it give Knauer any solace that Bruno had managed to evade not just his team but also the Finnish team and scores of police and wildlife officials who had been trying for nearly a month to neutralize him. Knauer had never experienced a bear like Bruno before, not so much because he was unlike other wild bears he had tracked and captured but because Bruno carried with him the hope of wilderness conservationists, the ire of public officials, and the adoration of millions of people. Knauer had never known such pressure; he had never seen such swirling media coverage, nor experienced such heightened tension among various stakeholders. He and his team had had little sleep over the past month. Without the unconditional support and resources of the Bavarian government, continuing his work would be futile. Calling off the capture attempt was not only prudent, it was necessary. He and his team simply had no more energy to give. Knauer admits today that the stress of the entire enterprise persisted for months afterward, robbing him of sleep for weeks after he had ended his attempts to capture Bruno. Without Knauer and his team, Bruno was basically on his own.

On June 24, the bear came within five feet of a person, a dangerous distance with any wild bear, let alone Bruno. Only a small spruce tree separated the two of them. The same day, two oblivious walkers strolling on a trail alongside a small lake failed to see Bruno standing knee-high in the water not thirty feet away. The event was caught on camera and became an instant sensation. Later, the bear approached a cabin, only to be confronted, strangely, by a group of cows who instinctively formed a wall and prevented the bear from advancing on the building. Bruno tried unsuccessfully to get past them before turning his attention to a small herd of sheep. He chased down one animal and mauled it as a local hunter looked on. A hiker, unaware of the situation, approached the area, but the hunter stopped him, and together, they left the scene unharmed.

A special team of highly trained hunters mobilized into action. A mix of police and former military, they carried high-caliber weapons with advanced scoping technology. They investigated a couple of locations, and when Bruno was found attacking another group of sheep in an alpine area known as the Kumpflalm, the team descended on the location and waited for him to make his next move. They did not have to wait long.

In the late evening, Bruno killed a sheep in another pasture, but, just as on the previous night, a group of young cows intervened. They formed a wall and pushed Bruno away. Despite several attempts to get to his prey, he eventually gave up and wandered into nearby cover.

The team of hunters moved swiftly to the location after a passerby reported the incident. They hunkered down in a cabin overlooking the area of the attack, hoping that Bruno would return after the cows moved to other pasture.

Throughout the night of June 25, the hunters remained vigilant. They watched the hillsides for any sign of Bruno, and they kept a close eye on the tree line, hoping to catch sight of him if he emerged from hiding. The night was cool, but not cold, and a slight breeze lifted up from the valley and swept along the open field. Even in the darkness, the bloodied body of the sheep stood out, a red-and-white mass of fur and flesh on the electric-green grass of early summer.

Members of the team took turns sleeping, drifting off as the night rolled by, but at least one team member's eyes remained on the slope throughout the night, scanning for any sign of Bruno. At 4:45 a.m. their patience paid off.

Bruno emerged from a nearby stand of woods, sniffing

momentarily into the night air before making his way toward the sheep he had mauled earlier.

Birds had already begun their morning rituals, and the valley was atwitter with activity. Bruno, unconcerned, ambled from the woods across the pasture at a casual pace, moving deliberately, but not hurriedly, toward his trophy. Whether he knew hunters were in the cabin probably did not matter. He had long since lost any fear of people.

One of the hunters in the cabin leveled a weapon at Bruno, taking aim out of a window. The hunter tracked the bear patiently, the barrel of the weapon following Bruno as he walked across the field. Chirps and bird calls filled the air, and the bear came into focus through the sight. The scope revealed the animal to be several hundred meters away, but the shooter was highly experienced, and the distance mattered little.

The shooter took a long, steady breath in and focused down the sight, and then, just as the first signs of morning light streaked above the mountains to the east, made the decision.

Slowly. Gently. With an even and deliberate motion, the hunter pulled the trigger and let out a breath.

The shot rang out, its echo filling the valley. The smell of gunpowder rose from the cabin. With only the slightest movement, the shooter looked up and peered into the morning light. Birds had fallen silent, and the hunter craned forward, looking for the quarry.

The morning air, hushed and damp, was still.

# PART III: THE LAST BEARS OF ABRUZZO

# 10

~~~~~~~~

# Italian Grizzlies

Paolo Ciucci leaned back in his chair, debating whether to place another call. It was the summer of 2006, and while Bruno romped through Germany, Ciucci was in the midst of a groundbreaking study of bears in Italy. He was, however, at his wits' end. There was only so much one person could do, especially when, for forty years, the managers of the National Park of Abruzzo, Lazio, and Molise (also known as PNALM or Abruzzo National Park) resisted input from scientists outside the region. Ciucci once again had been told "no" to further funding, and once again he had been saddled with a mound of bureaucratic forms, documents, permissions, and demands. If the stakes were not so high, he would have left the project years ago.

Ciucci, a large mammal biologist, was working from his office at the Charles Darwin Department of Biology and Biotechnology at the University of Rome (known as "La Sapienza"), where he had studied Italian bears for more than a decade. He conducted fieldwork across Italy, but it was his time in the central Italian national parks that had shaped his reputation: He was, essentially, the first scientist other than park naturalists to gain full access to the park and its animals. Before him, the park was effectively closed to the larger scientific community.

Ciucci trained in the United States. After studying at La Sapienza, he had two stints in the US, first in Minnesota in 1985 where he worked under Dave Mech of the US Geological Survey, from whom he learned wolf trapping techniques that he would later use in a study of wolves and feral dogs in Italy. Four years later he returned to pursue an MS in wildlife conservation and management at the University of Minnesota. Some of his studies were funded by a Fulbright award, and while in Minnesota, he traveled north to the Boundary Waters Canoe Area, paddling for several weeks with a quiet American guide whose silence he found at first unsettling and then inspired. He counts his time in the BWCA as a special moment in his career, when personal reflection and professional development converged and flowered into passion for the land, his research, and his life in general. A photograph of a canoe resting on a slab of Canadian shield, the stern of the boat still in the water, is pinned to one of his office bookcases. "My special place," he calls it, clearly enamored of the northern Minnesota wilderness.

Now he was back in Italy, working in the department that educated him as a young man and pursuing research he hoped would finally change the plight of rare animals in Italy. He'd earned a PhD while studying in Tuscany, and much of his initial research after returning to Rome was conducted alongside the legendary don of biological studies in Italy, Luigi Boitani. Boitani, who trained generations of biologists in Italy, enjoys the status of sage and master within the scientific community. With that comes a reputation outside of the community as a kind of gatekeeper into the field and, in the way that all legends surely insist, guardian of traditions of the old academy. He remains a formidable figure within Italian science, and his work enjoys wide recognition.

From the outskirts of Rome, the tallest peaks of the Apennines are visible on a clear, dry day, so field research was within a relatively short drive for Ciucci. Not satisfied simply working in a lab or crunching numbers on powerful computers, he felt the pull to get into the field in order to investigate the actual, on-the-ground conditions of his subjects. What he discovered was that the lab work and data analysis only told half the story. The other half emerged when local context revealed subtle reasons for surprising trends in data. In Abruzzo, so incredibly close to his office and lab in Rome, he discovered that human culture explained both the plight and the promise of a remarkable group of animals in the mountains of Abruzzo, among them wolves, chamois, and deer.

And, of course, bears.

The popular media liked to call them the "Italian grizzlies," and the label made some sense. The bears that Ciucci studied were, like the American grizzly, brown bears. Because the grizzly looms large in human imagination across national boundaries, labeling them "grizzlies" conjured images of massive and magnificent beasts and helped people understand that these wild bears were not the skittish black bears that traipsed through forests around the world. They were large, top-of-the-food-chain omnivores. But these brown bears were very different from American grizzlies—and the Slovenian bears in the Italian Alps—even if they were closely related. They were evolutionary oddities, testaments to a thousand years of adaptation to place and people. If they were Italian grizzlies, they were in fact more Italian than grizzly.

Brown bears, *Ursus arctos,* once roamed most of the northern hemisphere. Their range stretched from Kamchatka in Russia to the Urals and over to Ukraine, then south to the Caucasus. Given the bears' enormous range across Siberia, Russia adopted the bear as its national symbol. Bears lived, however, well beyond Russian borders, extending their footprint from China to Korea and southwest into the Himalayas, populating parts of both Nepal and Tibet. In central Asia, brown bears thrived from Afghanistan to Syria, and in north Africa, they inhabited the Atlas Mountains of Morocco, with reports placing them as far as Libya. In Europe, they virtually owned the mountains of Scandinavia, and in Finland, a tradition of bear hunting continues to this day. In central Europe, the bears maintained a strong presence in the Alps until the late nineteenth century, and their range extended all the way south to the tips of both Italy and Greece. Spain, France, and Germany all had native populations, and the high valleys of Andorra, a microstate in the Pyrenees, have recently seen the brown bear return to reclaim its original home.

Across the Atlantic, *Ursus arctos* occupied virtually all of Canada, and in Mexico a sizable population of *Ursus arctos* persisted until the early twentieth century. Confirmed reports of the Mexican brown bear continued into mid-century. Known for its silver fur, the bear was hunted even after it was listed as a protected animal, and the final documented killing of one occurred in 1976. Rumors persist to this day that a remnant group still hides in the mountains of Sonora, but like the Lord God bird of the American Southeast, evidence of the animal's existence has failed to materialize despite tantalizing hints that it persists.

In the US, the beast ranged from California to the Appalachians, with ancestors like the giant (more like enormous) short-faced bear being found in Alabama, South Carolina, and Florida. Archaeological evidence suggests that even into the nineteenth century, these bears freely roamed the central plains from the Dakotas to Oklahoma. Thomas Bangs Thorpe, a popular nineteenth-century writer, built his career on a widely read story about a brown bear in Arkansas—a work still anthologized in college literature textbooks today. Early accounts from the American Midwest, then called the Old Northwest, include tale after tale of encounters with brown bears, and a generation ago, Harold McCracken collected and related these tales in his now legendary cultural biography of the grizzly, *The Beast That Walks Like Man*. In North America, the prehistoric predecessors of the brown bear include a huge beast, larger than the widely known cave bear, that lived in the area that is now Los Angeles. It may have weighed a ton, and it represents the earliest record of the bear that would eventually evolve into *Ursus arctos*.

For Americans, few animals represent the American West better than the grizzly. The Old West was widely populated with brown bears, and most stories from the time focus on the animal's ferocity, a reputation that lingers to this day, despite relatively few deadly encounters each year. This is the beast that Lewis and Clark tangled with during their famous westward overland journey, and that tracked and killed Timothy Treadwell, the infamous "Grizzly Man." Its reputation emerges in popular movies, with the mythical beast tangling with both Alec Baldwin and Anthony Hopkins in *The Edge* and remorselessly mauling a helpless Leonardo DiCaprio in *The Revenant*. The North American grizzly represents both the unforgiving nature of the frontier and the fierce independence of the Western mind. It is little different in Italy and the rest of the world, where the brown bear represents unchecked savagery.

The expansive historical range of *Ursus arctos* demonstrates that it is an adaptable animal, perhaps unusually so given its position at the top of the food chain. Over millennia, the bear has survived in environments where other large carnivores perished. Arid regions, coastal rain forests, and alpine meadows have all hosted *Ursus arctos*. Today, we picture the brown bear as a beast of the mountains, but even at the turn of this past century, its range extended well outside the protected slopes of high mountains. In each corner of the northern hemisphere, some type of brown bear seemed to gain a foothold and evolve.

The various habitats around the world shaped the bear, giving each group distinct colors or shapes based on where it lived. In some instances, bears evolved into distinct subspecies, each with defining characteristics as unique as accents in human language.

The North American grizzly, for example, while closely related to the Russian Kamchatka bear, has habits and features derived from local environmental influences and opportunities. Similarly, the Syrian bear, smaller and less lumbering, probably evolved that way because its diet is so different from the Alaskan silverbacks. The bears of north Africa developed feeding habits more appropriate to arid regions than the bears that scavenged in Korea. And so it is that the *Ursus arctos* around the globe evolved and changed, often for reasons that are now lost to human history.

In Abruzzo, the brown bear evolved in especially distinctive ways. Because humans have long dominated the landscape, the bear has adapted to civilization over a time span that few other bears have experienced. Such long histories of human development affect bears directly through activities like hunting but also indirectly through agriculture, grazing, and the creation of trade routes. Inevitable changes show up both in the daily habits and the physical attributes of the bears, and they suggest that the Abruzzo bear, living alongside humans for longer than recorded history, is much more than just another grizzly, just another *Ursus arctos*. This animal is an artifact of human-beast interaction and an oddity of evolution that has no real comparison. Documenting the distinctiveness of the animal is the work of scientists like Ciucci.

Ciucci's timing in investigating the state of the Abruzzo bears could not have been better, both for his career and, more important, for the bears. As a young scientist returning from America, he knew he had to demonstrate the value of the type of fieldwork he was doing. He had a distinguished lineage in terms of his schooling, but he hoped to make an impact by bringing large-animal mammalogy to Italian animal science. His first forays were perhaps predictable for a person who conducted research in the area around Ely, Minnesota, home of the International Wolf Center; he launched his career in Italy by studying wolves from Tuscany to Umbria, calling on the knowledge he'd gained from his time in northern Minnesota. He had his eyes, though, on some of the larger, more exotic mammals in Abruzzo. He knew the mountains were home to a wide variety of native fauna, and he sensed that many of those animals lived in relative obscurity. What if, he wondered, he could bring his particular type of scientific inquiry to those animals? What might he discover? What kind of impact could he have?

The questions seem absurd in retrospect. Ciucci knew that the Abruzzo bears were relatively rare, and he knew that no one had bothered to make a reliable count of them in decades. All the information out there was either dated or grounded in hearsay, and he knew that simply providing an accurate, up-to-date census would be a service to the scientific community. What he did not know—or at least, what he did not fully appreciate—was precisely how important his counts would be and how significant his investigations into their lives and habits would be. What Ciucci demonstrated, better than anyone before, was not only that these bears were special and distinct but also that they were critically endangered and facing immediate threats to their survival.

Indeed, Ciucci has proven beyond all doubt that without help, the bears of Abruzzo face imminent extinction. Without action, they will disappear forever.

# 11

~~~

# Endangered Lives and Livelihoods

Saving an animal from extinction typically requires a range of interventions, but two key events must occur: official designation of the species as protected and public outcry for change. One does not necessarily rely on or result in the other, and one need not wait on the other to get rolling, but the fact is that without the former, the latter can be especially difficult to secure. Further, sometimes the official designation of a protected animal backfires and leads to public opposition to special mandates to protect the species. So while the official designation is often an important and crucial first step to save an animal from oblivion, these days it is also frequently a step into a political minefield whose contours are impossible to map or anticipate.

Examples of conflict surrounding preservation play out across small-town America on a daily basis. For instance, barely twenty years ago, construction at a popular and pricey ski resort in West Virginia skidded to a halt when a rare, protected salamander was discovered living on the western slopes of the resort. The Cheat Mountain salamander has been extirpated from the entire West Virginia highlands except for select slopes of Cheat Mountain, a massive geological structure whose ridge stretches nearly fifty miles. Snowshoe Mountain Resort lies at the intersection of Cheat Mountain and Back Allegheny Mountain, once home to a legendary stand of red spruce that has been eradicated through logging and development. With the loss of the red spruce came the loss of the Cheat Mountain salamander habitat, and, since 1989, at about the time when more extensive development of Snowshoe Mountain Resort began, the salamander has been included on the federal endangered species list. Snowshoe's recent rapid growth initially plodded along at a modest rate; in the early nineties, that rate accelerated, and it exploded at the beginning of the new millennium. The resort, owned then by Intrawest—a behemoth tour and hospitality company that developed the outrageously popular Whistler, Copper Mountain, and Mont-Tremblant—was hardly touched by the salamander discovery, but vacation-home owners on the western slopes suddenly faced scrutiny over property boundaries, building permits, and construction codes. Some real estate plats were declared unbuildable, left virtually worthless to the owners who had dreamed of building a ski chalet or selling the land for a handsome profit. Unsurprisingly, salamander fever hardly took hold on the mountain. Instead, outrage at upending the economic development and the dreams of vacation heaven simmered, and the salamander, instead of becoming a rallying point for a community, became an albatross. It remains so for many of the locals whose livelihoods depend on the success of the resort.

In the late 1980s and early 1990s, similar outrage over the Northern Spotted Owl, whose protection affected the logging industry in the Pacific Northwest, made international headlines, shining a spotlight on the issue of endangered species in a way that American citizens had never seen before. The controversy elevated the issue of preservation and created a national conversation about nature, labor, parks, and economic development.

At fourteen inches tall and notoriously quiet, the Northern

Spotted Owl nests high in mature forests, hunts at night, and generally minds its own business. Much like the salamander of West Virginia, it hardly seems like the central character in a major social conflagration. As with most owls, the Northern Spotted Owl rarely interacts with humans, but, unfortunately, *Homo sapiens* have a special love of the wood from the trees in which it nests. Logging helped establish and continues to drive economies of many Pacific Northwest towns, and even as old-growth forests have disappeared, newer woodlands provide a rich resource for local businesses. Yet older trees command greater value on the market, and they provide especially important raw materials for niche industries. Old-growth Douglas fir is ideal—and it is also the ideal habitat for spotted owls, who nest in trunks and sun themselves in high fir and cedar canopies.

Protecting the habitat of the Northern Spotted Owl meant American families who relied on logging suddenly found themselves without income. Bumper stickers like LOGGERS ARE AN ENDANGERED SPECIES TOO and PRESERVE THE SPOTTED OWL (IN FORMALDEHYDE) started appearing on vehicles, and rancorous debate filled local as well as national opinion pages. The *New York Times* gave the story significant coverage, resulting in a hail of letters, and the *Chicago Tribune*, which began covering the story as early as 1989, reported on local Oregonians wearing T-shirts that read Save a Logger, Eat an Owl. In October of 1990, the Stanford Marching Band formed into displays of a chainsaw and the face of an owl during the halftime show of their team's contest against the hosting Oregon Ducks. Boos from the crowd drowned out the announcer, and an apology from Stanford was followed by a one-game suspension for the band. The issue eventually became part of the 1992 presidential elections: At a time when blue-collar job losses were increasing across the country, the issue hit a nerve with labor groups, and the fight between timber interests and an owl forged surprising alliances across the political aisle. Indeed, the issue has never fully died away, and over the last twenty-five years, the tiny population of an obscure bird has pointed to the complex intersection of conservation, journalism, economics, and environmental policy.

The great gnashing of teeth over the Northern Spotted Owl offers a lesson for the preservation of a species because it illustrates how quickly local issues take on national significance when human economic interests are at odds with animal preservation. In Italy, similar intersections between conservation and industry animate discussion of various environmental issues, but for the Apennine bear, they are especially complicated for reasons that even people like Ciucci, who has dedicated much of his life to bear preservation, cannot easily explain. Italian environmental history is peppered with half measures and retrenchment largely derived from a history of laissez-faire oversight in local politics. Implementing plans to preserve a species depends on a local calculus that is difficult to compute. Adding the politics of international science, natural resource management, and Italian national governance to the equation only complicates the issues, making the political math virtually impossible to solve. International science, which has an unfortunate history of inept attempts to sway local or national dialogue on environmental issues, has an especially difficult case getting its voice heard within Italian communities. If international scientists have problems finding consensus on a particular issue, they have virtually no chance of facilitating change on the ground. In that case, even Italian scientists are hamstrung. How do they make a case for change if the international scientific community has failed to agree?

Attempting to protect a type of brown bear from extinction is, in some ways, far more difficult than attempting to save a one-of-a-kind creature, like the Tasmanian devil. Because there are not 100 subspecies of Tasmanian devils around the globe, people are more inclined to believe that it must be preserved. Pandas benefit from this phenomenon, as do manatees, the tiger, the polar bear, and especially colorful rare birds like the resplendent quetzal; because they have few or no living cousins, and because they *look* distinctive enough, if not outright bizarre enough, they warrant some sort of protection.

Yet all creatures are part of a vast, invisible web of life whose gossamer threads barely hold together life on Earth. Break too many, and the web collapses. However, convincing anyone to change behavior based on the notion of invisible, interconnected threads is incredibly difficult no matter the type of web one might imagine—whether it be in ecology, economics, human health, or family relationships. We prefer not to be reminded of our checking account balance when we are purchasing yet another colorful mixing bowl for our kitchens or new tie for our suits, nor do we care to be reminded of our cholesterol count and weight when we guzzle down a Mountain Dew, eat a handful of McDonald's fries, and finish off a bag of Twizzlers.

It is even more difficult to ask people to believe that they are actually part of the intersecting web of relationships, not outside of it. Making people believe that we dangle from invisible threads and live among them is asking them to change a fundamental individualism that insists that our idiosyncratic behaviors have limited impact on the world around us. Shifting from a perception of ourselves as something like a singular brain, which is responsible only for itself, to a more accurate image of each individual being more like a single neuron within an impossibly complex organism that includes the brain and other parts of the neural web stretched throughout our bodies requires a remarkable feat of imagination and humility. It requires acknowledging the paradox that despite our relatively tiny impact as individuals, the enormous systems in which we live still must shift and change to account for our impact. If we are persuaded of that, then our breaking of threads leads to the rather uncomfortable conclusion that we are severing our body's ability to communicate with other parts of itself, a process that leads to atrophy, disease, and disintegration, in the most fundamental meaning of those words.

We are not, in other words, simply destroying the lives of critters like owls and salamanders when we ignore the invisible lines connecting us all. We are, in fact, killing ourselves.

No one cares to hear that, no matter which system is at stake. It is hard to hear that your habit of drinking coffee in the morning might be ramping up your heart rate to dangerous levels, or that it might be leading to exploitive practices in Costa Rica. If such systemic impact is true, anything we might do could lead to disintegration. Each step we take may fracture the earth's crust, each relationship we form may prove the end of another. The consequences of the web analogy paralyze us or move us to hedonism, where our pleasure trumps all because the system is too big to manage or understand anyway.

Scientists working with endangered populations must account for systems when making their case to local communities, but it can be an incredibly hard sell. When they make the case to other scientists, however, they are doing very important work because they ensure that the first steps toward conservation occur. If science seems at times tone deaf to the concerns of a local population, it has incredibly keen ears for distant calls for help from within its own community. Those calls are the first movements toward transformation, so regardless of their impact on local communities, they are necessary in the long process of change.

The scientific and conservation establishment has not yet fully responded to the call to save the Abruzzo bears, in part because one of science's own invisible systems has not recognized it as worthy of intervention. The biological classification system that helps determine which species are most in need has yet to account for the distinctiveness of the Italian bears.

# 12

## Classifying Hope

Brown bears as a species are not endangered. Worldwide population is closing in on a quarter of a million animals, and within the scientific community, relatively few researchers feel any urgency to heed the calls to preserve a particular variety of brown bear. Given the relative health of *Ursus arctos* as a species, organizations that might otherwise step in to rally around a bear population and provide research funding instead turn their limited assets to supporting other, more obviously distinct species in decline. To change that, the Abruzzo bears will need to be recognized as something different. Doing that requires a name change.

For all of its reputation for cutting-edge innovation, the scientific community sometimes moves incredibly slowly to change well-entrenched ways of thinking. There is likely no better example of this than the classification system that, once put in place in the early nineteenth century, held sway over the scientific establishment ever since in fields such as biology, botany, etymology, and mammalogy. In the nineteenth century, classification fever gripped the natural sciences. Indeed, the sciences as we know them today were just being born, and early researchers often described themselves as involved in the field of "natural history," a catchall phrase that predates the slow segmentation of the sciences into increasingly specialized fields and subfields. Natural historians set about documenting the flora and fauna around the globe, and to do so they applied a classification system called the Linnaean system.

Most schoolchildren still learn the Linnaean system as "binomial nomenclature." Developed by Swedish botanist Carl Linnaeus, the system forms a tree of hierarchies that, in the nineteenth century, allowed explorers and natural historians to demonstrate relationships between types of animals. Species of animals are typically identified by the last two names of the hierarchy, hence "binomial," and they are given Latinate names. For example, humans are *Homo sapiens* ("wise man"), and polar bears are *Ursus maritimus* ("sea bear"). Some names derive from geography, such as the *Rattus norvegicus* ("Norway rat" or common brown rat), and others are named after their discoverer, such as *Propithecus verreauxi* ("Verreaux's sifaka" or lemur). The core words need not be actual Latin words, they need only be made Latinate.

The taxonomic system, even if not individual species within it, is readily recognized to this day, and some of its words have become part of everyday parlance. When we discuss a "species," we are in fact employing the lowest level of classification that Linnaeus identified. When we talk about a certain "genus" of animal, or which "family" of organisms a critter belongs to, we are invoking eighteenth-century taxonomies.

Mammalogists, of course, quickly adopted the system, and all species of mammal have a Linnaean name. *Ursus arctos* is Linnaean for brown bear, *Ursus americanus* for the skittish black bear, and *Ursus spelaeus* for the legendary and extinct cave bear. As science increasingly refined its ability to draw distinctions between groups of animals, the idea of subspecies emerged. Now, with the advent of genetic mapping, even more refinement has become possible. Indeed, genetic testing has resulted in some species being reassigned their place in the Linnaean hierarchy altogether as scientists learn that despite similarities in appearance, some animals that seem to be related have very little in common indeed. The best example of this is perhaps the giant panda. For years, the classification of the giant panda was up for grabs. Was it a bear or a raccoon? The debate revolved around the assignation of the red panda to its own distinct family, one that is more closely related to raccoons than bears. But genetic testing has affirmed that, in fact, the giant panda is more bear than anything else, and so it stands in the family *Ursidae*. Visual markers and even behavior, while useful, fail to fully express the breadth of species and the intricate set of relationships that exist on Earth.

The brown bear has not been immune from the incessant need to qualify and categorize. Early North American explorers noted regional differences between bears. The bears in Montana were especially large with long, narrow heads and were notoriously vicious. The bears in New Mexico were also large but supposedly had shorter heads that were, nonetheless, described as "massive."

These observations led one natural historian to the ambitious idea of classifying every type of regional brown bear in North America. C. Hart Merriam, whose expansive catalog remains infamous among bear ecologists, listed eighty-six different species of brown bears. The list was so extensive that even within relatively small geographical regions, Merriam identified several distinct species. For instance, Merriam identified at least three different species within Yellowstone. The grizzly (*Ursus horribilis*) roamed alongside the Yellowstone Park grizzly (*Ursus mirus*) and the Yellowstone Park big grizzly (*Ursus imperator*). As the names seemed to imply, the differences between the animals were subtle. The Yellowstone Park big grizzly was, predictably, larger than the Yellowstone Park grizzly, and could be identified easily only by examining skull samples. Indeed, skull samples were the foundation of many of the categorizations Merriam made, and he often paired a description of the skulls with historical observations to suggest when a bear might have been first seen. He made similar conclusions about presumably extinct bears. Having only skulls from which to theorize, Merriam extrapolated extravagant details about supposed species like the Navajo grizzly or the California coast grizzly.

The 1918 list, published as *Review of the Grizzly and Big Brown Bears of North America*, was untenable for a number of reasons, not the least of which was its complete failure to provide meaningful evidence beyond scant historical records and even more limited morphological samples to determine differences between bears. However, Merriam's list, and those of other species' enthusiasts, unwittingly helped foster a now well-entrenched but rarely discussed prejudice against renewed investigation of bear types, one that yokes bear ecology to traditions that have long since worn out their welcome. The audacity and the ridiculousness of Merriam has served as a kind of parable about the folly of overclassification, and to this day, resistance to securing subspecies designation among brown bears runs deep.

Currently, all brown bears are gathered under the classification of *Ursus arctos*, with fifteen official subspecies. For example, the North American grizzly is *Ursus arctos horribilis*, and the Eurasian brown bear is *Ursus arctos arctos*. But, of fifteen official subspecies, three are extinct, and another, the Tibetan blue bear, is largely extirpated due to demand for Chinese medicine derived from the bears. Most living Tibetan blue bears are believed to be in captivity, and no reliable counts of wild ones exist. Images and videos, often posted online, provide tantalizing evidence that they persist, but until a full accounting is made, no one will actually know. The result, then, is that for all practical purposes, only twelve subspecies of brown bears are recognized today, and one of those is hardly widespread. Other bears, no matter how distinctive or demonstrably different, are registered as geographical variations or regional hybrids.

The method of labeling the types of bears is important because research funding is often linked, directly or indirectly, to species classification. Further, conservation activists rely on scientific classifications to formulate preservation legislation or policy initiatives. As a result, the expansion of any list of species or subspecies faces deep skepticism—much of it healthy, but some needlessly recalcitrant— and political resistance. Because funding, resource allocation, and reputations infiltrate taxonomic systems, the process of changing them becomes as much a rhetorical process as a scientific one—a case of persuasion that must accommodate not only science but also cultural and political savvy.

For the best, but not only, chance of survival, the Abruzzo bear likely needs to be returned to a classification that was stripped from it a half a century ago. Even simply a refinement of the taxonomic status of the animal would help. To be correctly classified is to be honored as worthy of attention, and only that special binomial designation can provide a species the fullest protection available. The nomenclature matters because research is deeply wed to it. So is money.

In other words, one of the Abruzzo bears' best hopes for preservation rests in their name. And getting that name right.

# 13

*Ursus arctos marsicanus*

In the eighteenth-century humorous novel *Tristram Shandy*, Laurence Sterne relates a tongue-in-cheek theory of names and naming. Walter Shandy, the father of the soon-to-be-born Tristram, asserts that the name of a child inevitably determines that child's future. Tracing an absurd causal relationship between a name and the future prospects of a person, Walter Shandy declares that "good or bad names ... irresistibly [impress] upon our character and conduct." He offers "Judas" as an example, declaring that giving a child the name "Judas" inevitably dooms him to failure. For Walter, only one name would be less desirable: Tristram. The reader is left to imagine how the narrator, Tristram himself, came to be saddled with the name his father so loathed.

While names in the taxonomic system that governs scientific classification do not inherently impress goodness or evil upon a species (as they do for poor Tristram), they do have remarkable power in shaping an animal's future. A distinct name and the significance attached to it, while not a panacea, would go a long way in helping the Abruzzo bears receive the attention they need. To be recognized as distinct requires bucking the tide of standard practice today, which is, in terms of bears, to minimize differences. The Abruzzo bears, simply put, cannot be considered another adaptive oddity, a regional population being extirpated from a geographic region. If they are recognized as the last of their kind, then scientists, ecologists, and conservationists might be rallied to make a last, desperate bid to ensure the animal's survival.

Paolo Ciucci has become one of the most important voices for the bears. While he does not identify reclassifying Abruzzo's brown bears as the goal of his research, it is clear that his work will be used to make that case. Ciucci knows that reclassification could drive greater funding for research and ensure greater protections for the bears, but he also knows that the immediate conservation needs of the bears require other interventions. Ciucci takes as his goal, then, the careful documentation and analysis of the bears and their habitat, and his research, as well as that of others working with the bears, demonstrates rather convincingly that there is something quite different about these particular bears—something worthy of a name.

The Abruzzo bears had, until the middle of the twentieth century, been considered a distinct subspecies: *Ursus arctos marsicanus*. Named after Mount Marsicano, a mountain that rises some 7,300 feet above the Sangro River Valley in the heart of Abruzzo National Park, the bears were first officially categorized in 1921. Their home range to this day includes the area around Mount Marsicano, though they once roamed throughout Marsica, a region of Abruzzo once home to the Marsi, an ancient tribe of people whose territory extended further north to the city of Avezzano and east to the stunning village of Scanno and beyond. The Marsi, despite some local Abruzzese claiming them as ancestors, are long since gone. Their namesake region and bears managed to outlive them. The Marsican bear was demoted in a flurry of activity in the middle of the century to simplify the designations of types of bears.

Ciucci's research provided long-needed estimates of the population of the Marsican bears, a.k.a. the Abruzzo bears. For decades, no reliable count of the bears existed, with numbers ranging from nearly 100 in the early to middle part of the twentieth century to perhaps only thirty as the millennium approached. In 2008, however, Ciucci, his mentor Luigi Boitani, and their collaborators provided an important, field data–driven estimate that followed from an initial, admittedly incomplete survey earlier in the decade. Using an analytic method called the Huggins model, the researchers entered data from multiple types of evidence of bear activity, including hair samples, scat samples, and tree rubbings. Especially helpful were hair samples collected from buckthorn patches. Buckthorn produces fall berries that the bears adore, so scientists place hair snags and traps in the bushes to capture samples as bears ramble through. The collected samples are then analyzed to identify how many different bears were in the area. The goal is to identify specific bears in order to avoid double-counting animals. Through DNA analysis of hair, scat, and previously captured animals, Ciucci, Boitani, and the others were able to use the Huggins modeling system to provide a precise and highly accurate bear count.

The numbers they offered were not encouraging. Their evidence pointed to forty-three bears.

Though the researchers strongly cautioned that that number may have been low, as the available data and analytic models were limited, it was nonetheless a startling number. A more refined and precise survey, conducted in 2011, suggested the number was fifty-one. In 2014, yet another study led by Ciucci put the number at fifty, with an estimated twenty-two males and twenty-eight females, including cubs. Breeding females were estimated as numbering around ten to twelve adults. All these studies demonstrate that, hovering around fifty with no signs of increase despite (admittedly ad hoc) attempts to encourage population growth for nearly three decades, the bears face, as Ciucci and his collaborators have said, "a persistently high extinction risk."

Knowing the actual population demonstrates the precariousness of the bear population in concrete terms, but before the flurry of activity in the early 2000s, much of it by Ciucci or his collaborators, there were even more glaring information gaps that prevented a systematic recovery effort. While local Abruzzese knew the bears' habits and could testify to certain features and preferences of the bears, no systematic study had been conducted to demonstrate things as basic as what the bears ate and where the bears most liked to den. The local knowledge, important as it is, is insufficient to mobilize either the scientific community or people outside of Abruzzo, both of which need to be involved if the bears are to be saved.

Those gaps have started to be filled. Work by Giovanna Di Domenico, who worked with Ciucci and others on a food-habit study, affirmed what so many locals knew—that the bears gorged on buckthorn berries in the fall and scavenged for ants throughout much of the spring and summer. They also consumed large volumes of "forbs." *Forb* is a catchall term for a type of vegetation. In the same way that "grasses" refers to a wide range of plants, forbs represent a wide variety of what most people would consider weeds—fleshy-stalked, flowering plants, like ragweed or poison oak. In Abruzzo, forbs include plants like wild carrots, and they are full of protein. Leading up to buckthorn season, bears consume huge quantities of forbs.

While likely unsurprising to many naturalists, the brown bears' diet of fruits and vegetables comes as a surprise to most people. The image of the brown bear as a vicious beast is so ingrained in the human collective imagination that reorienting the mind is difficult. Even the North American grizzly spends most of its days pulling up roots, munching on leaves, and scraping berries from bushes. Such behavior is hardly befitting its subspecies moniker *Ursus arctos horribilis*, which conjures images far more vicious than its dietary preferences and requirements.

The bears' appetites for buckthorn berries and their behavioral habits that derive from the fall gorge on them provide tantalizing clues as to what makes this species so special. The Abruzzo bears are even more reliant on vegetation than the *horribilis*. An extensive study of the Abruzzo bears' diet suggests that few have any inclination toward devouring meat. Though some studies suggest that most species of bears seek out meat in spring seasons, the Abruzzo study did not include spring collections, so it comes with a decided asterisk next to its findings. Still, the meat that the Abruzzo bears might consume would, in fact, be carrion. Rarely would the bears slay large mammals, such as sheep or deer or similar animals in the region. Small mammals like mice show up with some regularity in their scat samples, but they hardly account for even 5 percent of the food volume. In general, the Abruzzo bears, even more so than their North American cousins, eat plants, ants, nuts, and berries to get by in the world. They are essentially vegetarians.

It should be no surprise, then, that though the Abruzzo bears range in the mountains, their preferred space to roam is in the beech forests of the Apennines. There, forbs and nuts are readily available, and at the edges of clearings, where wild carrots and celery grow, the bears can be found lounging in the sun between forest feasts. Though the buckthorn of the fall grows a bit farther up mountainsides, the bears spend most of their time wandering the woods and clearings in the valleys. They den in them. They forage in them. And they hide in them.

Abruzzo National Park is home to what is believed to be southern Europe's oldest beech forest. One swale between the mountains includes trees some 500 years old. There, the great trees shade out any understory, and in the fall, a blanket of leaves smothers any wayward sapling or weed. In quiet places like this—one of the few inaccessible by road in the middle of Italy—the bears can wander unharassed with their favorite foods readily available.

Ciucci has found in recent examinations of bear diets that the consumption of buckthorn berries may be trending downward. This is likely due to a degradation of bear habitat. Fewer buckthorn bushes, cleared for any number of reasons from the edges and even interior of the park, mean fewer berries, a food that is important for the bears as they begin to den for winter. While the bears, as Ciucci and his collaborators note, make up for dwindling buckthorn berries by supplementing with other fruits in the area, they nonetheless appear to be facing additional pressures on their survival. Nutritional pressure can do as much to undermine animal populations as direct human intervention, even if the impact is slower and less easily recognized.

All bears gorge as winter approaches, and they do so on a wide range of energy-producing plants. In the Canadian Rockies, for instance, the bears spend days on end gobbling down huckleberries, buffalo berries, and blueberries, and their behavior can be linked not only to their latent biological impulses—those that make them act like bears—but also to the land that nourishes them. Merriam's absurdly long list of eighty-six subspecies of brown bears is linked, in no small part, to the behavioral traits that bears in each region exhibit. Those behaviors have helped shape, and then in turn were shaped, by physical changes in the bears. In other words, as the bears adapt to their locale, their bodies change. When shifts in the land are slow and a species like the Abruzzo bear settles into a region over a period of centuries, the animal becomes inextricably linked to the resources in that area. If land changes happen quickly, the bears cannot adapt. Most animals cannot. Rapid change spells doom for most species.

The well-publicized plight of the giant panda is a good example. Part of the problem with panda survival is its specialized diet; pandas rely on certain bamboo for much of their nutrition. Similarly, the koala in Australia has a highly specialized diet focused on eucalyptus. The diet of the Abruzzo bears is not nearly as specialized, but they are wed to the land in the same ways, and their bodies demonstrate it.

In 2012, a study headed up by Paolo Colangelo, who worked

alongside Ciucci, demonstrated in as firm a way as possible that the skulls of the Apennine brown bears are especially distinct. Smaller in general stature than most brown bears, the Abruzzo bears have heads that are broader at the cheekbones and across the forehead. The area just behind the cheekbones is also enlarged, contributing to a flatter, wider head. The front molar teeth are slightly flatter, resulting in greater space within the mouth. These differences, first systematically described by Anna Loy and her collaborators in 2008, support the decades-old contention that these bears not only look different from most brown bears; they actually *are* different. This demonstrates that they have mutated either because they are isolated and thus have fewer genetic variations, or because they have faced distinctive pressures on their development, or both. The skull shape suggests that the Abruzzo bears have evolved to feed almost exclusively on vegetation. The muscles for chewing, trained over millennia to crush and grind plant matter, developed in ways that the skull then reflects.

This physical distinctiveness is not alone sufficient to demonstrate that the Abruzzo bears are worthy of official subspecies categorization. But when it is added to the context of bears that are notoriously docile and have been isolated from any other bear populations for at least 600 years, and likely more than 1,500 years, it leads researchers like Loy and Ciucci to advocate for reconsideration of the bears' taxonomic status. If a bear looks different from other bears, acts differently, and is even on the level of bone structure shaped differently, it surely, at the very least, should be *considered* for reclassification. The main issue will be, as always, whether the bears' genetic makeup is as distinctive as its physical attributes. Are the bears, on a cellular level, significantly different from other *Ursus arctos*?

They appear to be. Though science is years away from being definitive on the matter, several studies under way suggest variations of the bears at the genetic level, and earlier studies suggested mitochondrial differences. Until the new studies are released, however, those making a case for the distinctiveness have to rely on behavioral and physical differences that are more readily identified and described. Regardless of scientific findings, for people like Ciucci, the real point is not reclassification but data-driven assessment for the need for preservation of a unique species with a remarkable history and connection to humans.

Much of the information now emerging about the bears of Abruzzo is new, at least to the more rigorous scientific community. Because Abruzzo National Park so closely guarded the population, and because the management of the park for many years prohibited outside scientists from systematically investigating them, information was scarce. Now, though, that has changed. The foundational data that Ciucci and others like him have compiled and published is invaluable not only in academic terms but also in pragmatic terms. It helps mount a case for the distinctiveness of the bears. Even if, as Ciucci has argued, chasing reclassification is a fool's game because it ultimately distracts from the pressing need to address the basic uniqueness of the animal's geographic adaptation, it may still help create change in human attitudes toward the bears. Perhaps most crucially for international aid and intervention, it prompts science to reorient to account for its significance in the animal world.

Taken together, the research suggests with remarkable force that these bears are different. Different from the brown bears in America. Different from the brown bears in Russia. Different from the bears in China, Morocco, and Mexico, and even the ones just to the north in Austria, France, and eastern Europe. They are even different from another group of brown bears in Italy, the group from which Bruno sprung and that shaped European discussion about bears for the last decade.

All these differences, long observed in the Abruzzo bears, have only recently received the attention they deserved. While early observers of the bears noted the remarkable differences between these bears and other brown bears, no systematic attempt to demonstrate distinctiveness occurred until relatively recently. The reason was not for lack of interest. Instead, it was due to the wishes of one man who strived above all other things to preserve Abruzzo's bears. In a cruel twist of fate, his actions may have done the opposite.

His name is Franco Tassi. His love of the Abruzzo bears is legendary, but his methods of "preservation" may have unwittingly allowed malevolent forces to gather at the boundaries of the park. They are forces that have now laid siege to the land.

And to the bears.

# 14

## The King Who Launched a Movement

Franco Tassi ruled Abruzzo National Park like a fiefdom for more than thirty years. During that time, he lifted the park to international prominence even while he blocked most attempts to study the bears in a systematic, scientifically rigorous way. One part saint, one part villain, Tassi was known then for his passion to preserve the region, and even to this day his enemies admire his profound love of the park and the Abruzzo wildlife. Exuding quintessential Italian charm, he is a man who is quick to smile and able to carry on a conversation with just about anyone. He has an ability to finesse complicated exchanges yet draws firm lines around issues of conservation. During his tenure at the helm of Abruzzo National Park, he forged alliances with conservationists and parks around the world, and, largely through the force of his own will, he built the reputation of the park, moving it from dinky backwater to international sensation. He nurtured relationships with prominent conservationists around the globe, and in doing so made Abruzzo National Park a model of a certain vein of conservation that many now consider old-fashioned and outdated but that at the time was revolutionary and innovative. Those relationships also made him a king virtually impossible to unseat from his throne.

Now, however, the former director lives in a residential enclave, Casal Palocco, west of Rome. Casal Palocco is dotted with gated communities and small commercial and shopping hubs. Winding roads trace through neighborhoods and parks, and bougainvillea climbs walls and fences, fuchsia and pink blossoms reaching for the sun. Developed in the 1950s and '60s by a prominent architect known for what would be called Italian Rationalism, the villas of Casal Palocco were intended to unite families by providing broad living space that also connected them to neighbors through open-air constructions, porticos, and gardens. Futuristic-looking in a sometimes kitschy way, the buildings are extravagant in their use of space and broad features, so that their egalitarian appeal is merged with a sense of grandeur. This is where Tassi settled, a once forward-looking place fit for a king who imagines himself a person of the people. He rarely returns to Abruzzo.

Tassi and his wife, Margherita, live comfortably here, but in Tassi's home one senses his yearning for the park. Despite the clean, strong lines of his community's villas and the relatively sparse decorations of his neighbors, his house is surrounded by rich plantings and a green lawn crowded with dense shrubbery. Stepping stones—not a concrete pathway as with most of the houses—lead to his front door, and his front porch blooms with flowers of all kinds. Margherita is the green thumb and prides herself on the aesthetics that her plantings provide. Vines grow along columns, and hanging baskets brighten a pergola sheltering the front door with red, orange, and purple. It is, in all, a temperate jungle, a wilderness inside one of the first planned developments in all of Italy.

The interior of Tassi's home evokes more of that same yearning for nature. Every corner, every small space, is populated with a memory—of the park, of his work as a naturalist, or of his life with Margherita as the first family of Abruzzo National Park. The living room is tall, wide, and open, with bookcases climbing nine feet high. On their shelves are tomes about wildlife from around the world and artifacts of Tassi's travels and his loves—animals, insects, and the diversity of nature. Displays of shimmering blue butterflies pinned in cases flank a window casement, and stunning antique tiles—blue and yellow and painted with animals from the parks—decorate a wall adjacent to his kitchen. The entire room is a testament not just to a career in nature but to his profound love of the animals and the wilderness. And among the things he loved most—indeed still loves—are the bears of Abruzzo.

His home has plenty of reminders of the bears. On a small pedestal in a prominent position next to a staircase, a vase is decorated with a naive painting of a bear standing on its hind legs, its forearms stretched up and out—a statement piece highlighting the core of much of Tassi's career: the Abruzzo bear. And as the vase illustrates with its crazed surface and stylized imagery, it is an ancient Italian bear, a special holdover from an older time.

"It was a gift," Tassi says, acknowledging both the vase and the ancient beast painted on it. "The bear is always a beautiful gift."

His voice trails off. His mind is elsewhere, but his face betrays an expression of certainty, of steadfast assurance. When he speaks again, it is as though he is speaking to someone who would doubt him or call into question his dedication or integrity. He seems to be speaking to someone who has never bothered to know him.

"I love the park," he says with conviction. "I will always love the park."

He has good reason to feel such devotion to it. He led the park for most of its dramatic expansion in the second half of the last century, overseeing and in many respects directing Italy's movement to preserve wild places. Though he inherited a park that had been in existence for nearly forty years, under Tassi, Abruzzo National Park and indeed the entire park system in Italy changed significantly.

The Italian park system first emerged in the early twentieth century during a fifty-year period of global conservation activity that saw the creation of most of the world's national parks. The United States initiated the movement to protect wilderness for public use, but national park fever spread overseas quickly. In 1909, just as Teddy Roosevelt, who was responsible for some of America's greatest park achievements, was finishing his tenure as President of the United States, Sweden established Europe's first national parks. The country formed nine parks in one year alone, some of them to protect islands, others to protect glaciers, and still others to protect entire habitats within the Scandinavian mountains. Switzerland, recognizing the foresight of the conservation movement as it grew in northern Europe, protected some of its own mountains in 1914, and though some European nations debated the value of a park system, the first half of the twentieth century still witnessed tremendous growth of public land management throughout Europe and the Americas.

The first motions to start a national park in Italy began in 1912 within the mountains of central Italy in Abruzzo. The mountain landscape hosts a famously proud local people who anticipated the need to protect the land from outsiders. The native Abruzzese recognized that protecting the mountains also meant protecting their culture, one that had always imagined itself both the product and the guardian of the land, so sequestering part of the land as park preserved not just local flora and fauna but local culture as well.

Abruzzo National Park was the first national park created in Italy. It was formed as a private preserve between 1910 and 1920, when a mere three square miles were protected through the generosity of a nobleman and a group of concerned citizens. In the years that followed, the parkland began to grow, and in 1921, it became Italy's first national park. Abruzzo National Park grew rapidly over the century, expanding to nearly 200 square miles of protected mountain habitat. By the early 1990s, a newly empowered environmental movement pushed hard for further protection of various ecosystems within the Abruzzo region. To the south and east of Abruzzo National Park, Majella

National Park was created in 1993. Majella, the central mountain that is the park's namesake, has been called the "Mother Mountain" for generations, and the people in the region have long been known for their acceptance of the whims of mother nature and her mountains.

In the summer, the relatively modest number of Italian tourists who eventually find their way to Abruzzo's parks congregate in the valleys, usually for short day trips. Pescasseroli, which sits in a valley within Abruzzo National Park, is a town of maybe 2,000 throughout most of the year, but during a brief period in the summer, as Italians escape cities, it swells, according to some, to nearly 20,000 in the middle of some days. A few yards from the main square, the Abruzzo National Park headquarters offers tourists a small zoo and cultural center. Visitors can stroll through exhibits of archaeological discoveries, fossils and bones, and taxidermied birds and mammals. Outside the center, a small park is surrounded by plantings of native flora, small enclosures housing roe deer, native wolves, and one of only two Abruzzo bears in captivity.

Though less than fifty miles from Rome—not even a ninety-minute drive—the mountains of Abruzzo are effectively a continent away, culturally and politically, from the rest of the country. In Pescasseroli, locals rarely travel beyond nearby communities, and virtually none speak English. Unlike in Rome or Florence, few restaurant menus or store signs provide English translations for tourists. The Abruzzese, proud of their heritage, will not bend to the whims of, in their minds, a sterilized Western culture. Even many Italians find themselves feeling like outsiders when they travel to the area. The region remains isolated, with many of its towns inaccessible by rail links. Italians, who in some abstract way treasure their parks and are proud of them, continue to see the place as decidedly backward, certainly not worthy of much consideration. The housing prices, which are thousands of dollars below regions like Umbria or Tuscany, reflect this. The land prices, also incredibly low, reflect this, as does the fact that even Italian tourists who bother to come typically stay briefly. Abruzzo may be a green gem in the mind of many Italians, but, like an emerald, it is rarely preferred over the glimmering diamonds of Italy's more famous regions and cities.

Abruzzo rarely makes national or international headlines. The massive 2009 earthquake in L'Aquila, the capital city of Abruzzo, drew global attention briefly, but in general, the region is forgotten. Throughout the twentieth century, it witnessed an extensive flight of its population, with nearly 1.3 million Abruzzese leaving. Many moved overseas, nearly a quarter of them settling in New York. The New York immigrants have kept alive their connections to the land, but as with so many Italian expatriations, the stories of their past remain locked within their communities, lost to the rest of the world.

Among the stories that have been forgotten is the story of Italy's conservation movement. Franco Tassi was at the center of it, and more than one person has suggested that he single-handedly created it. If that is the case, Tassi formed in Abruzzo an environmental ethic that resonated around the world.

# 15

## Hagiography

Franco Tassi yearns to be remembered.

Sitting at his dining room table, he surrounds himself with folders and albums and books about his time as park director. When he lifts one and begins to page through it, his eyes light up and memories take shape, real and present.

"Here," he says, pointing to an image of a group of park rangers. "That's me. And he"—Tassi points to one of the men standing next to him—"he worked for me as a park ranger for many years. All of these men did. You can meet him." Tassi keeps his finger on the first man he identified in the photograph, slightly shorter than Tassi and wearing a khaki uniform and a hat that looks like a cross between a baseball cap and a vintage French military cap. Also khaki, the hat has a green-and-gold park logo on it. Tassi persists: "You can talk to him. He can tell you what important work we did. He lives in Opi. You can find him there. Ask at the café just as you enter town."

The papers and books spread across the table are a testament to Tassi's years in the park. Perhaps more important, they are also a testament to his commitment to the preservation of Abruzzo's bears. Most of the paperwork references the bear, and much of it deals exclusively with the animal. Tassi published several books during his tenure as director, providing not only histories of the park but also of his ongoing attempts to preserve and expand the bear population. The books detail early trappings of young cubs, the chasing off of poachers from the park, and even the feeding of animals high in the alpine habitat to prevent them from coming into human contact. In one of his books, a photo titled "Operation 'In the Bear's Mouth'" shows a helicopter flying into the mountains with an enormous net in tow. In the net, Tassi explains, is a hoard of apples and other rich food for the bears.

"We took the food to them in the fall, before they sleep for the winter. We flew it up to them to keep them away from the town and the farms. It was good for the bears. It made them fat for the winter."

As he reminisces, Tassi makes a not-so-subtle point about his career as director. His stories, both as he tells them and as they emerge in his written documents, establish not only the significance of the bears and the need for their preservation, but also his centrality in leading the park to national and international acclaim. His stories pay homage to the park, certainly, but they also paint the picture of a saint—a forward-looking and at times hard-nosed one, but a saint nonetheless. That part of the story is what Tassi wishes others would remember.

Certainly, he remains a legendary figure in the park system, with good reason. Tassi was an international sensation who could count many important milestones as feathers in his cap. At the time he took over Abruzzo National Park, less than 1 percent of Italy's land was dedicated to conservation. Envisioning more green space, Tassi announced a nationwide initiative to go to 10 percent. He made Abruzzo National Park the starting place by using it to highlight the value of preservation, and he rallied conservationists to push the government for more parks. By the 1990s, his vision (though not his alone) came to fruition. Italy became a country with more than 10 percent of its land dedicated to parks. Few countries can boast such an achievement, and no other person can claim to have made such a single-handed contribution except, perhaps, John Muir or Teddy Roosevelt.

Smaller but no less significant successes also mark his career. Under Tassi's watch, the native wolf population grew swiftly, and it now enjoys a stable series of packs that roam different parts of the park. He led an initiative to create an "emerald necklace" of parkland that would connect the north and south of Italy with a series of national parks—an initiative which, while never fully completed, led to the expansion of his own park to include land from the provinces of Lazio and Molise and the establishment of the Gran Sasso and Monti della Laga National Park and the Majella National Park in Abruzzo.

Tassi also forged important international relationships, bringing experts from a number of fields to the park to show them what was possible when focus and fire drives innovation. He commissioned and led studies that demonstrated that parks could be valuable assets to a region and that they could bring economic development to poor areas. He continues to brag that when he was park director, some towns left for dead were resurrected, with new economic life breathed into them by dedication to a vision of preservation. He argues passionately to this day that under his leadership, local people and the park learned how to work together and that tensions between local families and park management were ameliorated, not by placating traditionalists but instead by showing younger people what a renewed devotion to nature could bring them. In Tassi's mind, and he is probably at least partially right, park villages thrived because he showed them a new vision of themselves. Indeed, the entire park system thrived on his watch, and it is for that reason that he simply cannot understand why he has been forgotten and why his legacy has been so cruelly cast aside and written out of the history books.

He wants his legacy recovered, if not entirely renewed. He wants his contributions to the Italian park system to be remembered. He wants to be recognized as the trailblazer that he was, but it will be difficult to do. Despite his extraordinary success at Abruzzo National Park, his career as director ended in scandal.

# 16

Erasure

Tassi was effectively erased from the history books in 2002 when he became the subject of an extensive and widely publicized criminal investigation. The first parts of it seemed innocuous enough, but as the investigation continued, more and more accusations came to light, and he was ousted from the park. He has never regained his prominence.

Tassi's tremendous fall from grace began when a secret recording device was reportedly found in a room where park managers and committees met. In a neighboring room, Tassi's accusers maintain, audio equipment—including several tapes full of private conversations—was discovered, all connected by wire to at least three bugs in committee chambers. The recording equipment was linked to Tassi, who had supposedly grown paranoid that others were trying to unseat him as director. He was partially correct. Some park staff and politicians had grown weary of his management and wanted him removed from office. The purported spying and bugging of the office provided the contingency they needed to act. Tassi was unceremoniously dismissed as director of Abruzzo National Park.

At the time of his dismissal, and likely as a result of the stress induced by fighting for his position against allegations of misuse of park funds, Tassi was convalescing in a hospital while being treated for a heart condition. He received news of his firing while in bed at the hospital.

He remains angered and hurt by the timing of the announcement, insisting that as a longtime servant of the park, he deserved at least to be given a chance to hear the complaints in person and to defend himself. But the reasons for such an inglorious dismissal likely were a result of other allegations against him that were emerging.

At the heart of the scandal were claims of embezzlement and abuse of power. Aside from the seedy accusations of spying on committees with bugs, opponents of Tassi alleged that he sluiced money from park coffers and directed it to his own pockets by setting up satellite organizations that would financially benefit from his management. Governmental prosecutors could not ignore those claims, and by 2003, legal proceedings to prosecute began.

In findings from his ultimate conviction, the extent of Tassi's mismanagement (to some) or tyranny (to others) became clear. Tassi had set up a park office in Rome for the ostensible purpose of park advocacy in the nation's capital. The prosecution argued that Tassi essentially used the Rome "office" as a personal retreat where he would write off unapproved costs connected to park activities. They further argued that Tassi used a park Diner's Club credit card to make personal purchases, and that even after he was fired, he commandeered a park Mercedes and a van for his own personal use. They even argued that Tassi had essentially stolen a library's worth of books and materials from the park that could be valued at nearly $10,000. They accused him of inappropriately paying staff for working on his own personal projects and for his wife in her attempts to beautify the park; Margherita was named as a defendant in some of the proceedings. When the final sum of Tassi's misdeeds was calculated, the prosecution claimed —and the courts affirmed—that Tassi and one of the former park presidents had profited on the order of €900,000—at the time, nearly $1.7 million. In 2003, after having been ousted on March 3, 2002, Tassi was ordered by a court of auditors to pay the entire amount back.

Five years later, Tassi was convicted of embezzlement. The conviction resulted in more fines and a devastating criminal sentence: three years in prison, followed by a lifetime ban from serving in any public office or service. Among the fines levied was an especially bitter one that struck Tassi at his heart: He was ordered to pay €20,000 in reparations to the Abruzzo National Park to help it repair its public image.

As Tassi fought for his reputation, the ensuing legal battles were at turns nasty and mind-numbingly technical. Tassi appealed virtually every ruling, and court cases dragged on for years. Tassi's tremendous success as a park director made his fall from grace a spectacle—the media swarmed during his ouster and trials because, as an Italian with an international reputation, he had apparently disgraced his office and his country. Much of the coverage seemed personal, voyeuristically obsessed with the details and minutiae, and it laid waste to Tassi's image. By contrast, Tassi's appeals remained on the margins of reporting, despite the fact that some of them seemed to vindicate him.

Tassi won appeals. Many of them. His attorneys raised doubts about the veracity of the reported bugging of park meeting rooms, and key documents that purportedly demonstrated his abuses vanished. By the time it was all said and done, Tassi's jail sentence had been dropped to two years, which he could serve at home, and the fee meant to chastise him for ruining the reputation of the park and "engender[ing] serious distrust of institutions from the citizens, even more so in times of economic crisis when they are burdened by high tax burden," was cut in half. His banishment from public office was also changed from a lifetime to a two-year moratorium on serving in any official capacity in the state.

Though Italy's Supreme Court ruled in 2012 that Tassi's appeals were inadmissible to their chambers and could go no further than they already had, Tassi is in many ways still fighting the damage done to his legacy. He continues to speak publicly about the events that led to his demise, and he regularly posts opinion pieces that reference the events on websites or blogs. When some new public scandal surfaces, he draws comparisons to his unjust prosecution, seeing in contemporary events signs of the same sort of malicious coups that flung him from office. He also pens invectives against the current park management, decrying their leadership and invoking images of the glorious past when he led the park.

The lingering resentment that is so prevalent in his writings does not come out in person. When giving talks or while conversing face-to-face, he charms. He extolls the virtue of nature and parkland, and he insists on tracing the important work of preservation. He highlights his role, certainly, but the venom that emerges in his writing remains in the background, if it even exists at all. He remains sincerely baffled that anyone would try to remove him from the park, let alone that they would be successful, and while he knows that some in the Italian environmental community disagreed with him, he seems surprised that some people so deeply dislike him and that others genuinely fear him. Or, at least, that they did before he was forced out.

"The park was nothing, a wasteland, before I came," he says. It's a sentiment he repeats often in person and in print, and he is, in some respects, right. So he is unconcerned that his "enemies" feel he may have played too fast and loose with the rules or that his park leadership created dysfunctional systems marked by favoritism and distrust. For Tassi, love of the park and nature trumps any possible negative outcomes of his actions. His intent, in his mind profoundly and deeply altruistic, justified his method of rule.

That method was at the very least autocratic, if not outright dictatorial. While Tassi would never figure himself a dictator, many who worked under him would. A benevolent dictator for some, a vengeful, score-keeping one for others, but a dictator nonetheless. Regardless of the label, Tassi clearly savored his role as the man in charge. He was the leader. The trailblazer. The head guy. *Il direttore.*

And he abided no interlopers.

# 17

## Control

Tassi is perhaps unaware of how many people still admire him. Many townspeople in villages throughout the park yearn to see him or someone like him return. For them, Tassi brought a sense of pride to being part of the park. As Marco di Bona, a hotelier and native to Pescasseroli, says, "He was good for us. When Tassi was here, the parks were important. We were respected."

Di Bona is right inasmuch as Tassi brought international acclaim to the park system. Even in his ouster, groups across Europe and the US lobbied for his reinstatement. A group of university faculty signed an open letter that decried his removal from office, and letters and petitions from the Americas were directed to the Italian government. Some advocates even wrote to Silvio Berlusconi, then the Italian prime minister, asking for intervention. A group of naturalists from the Adirondack parks in the US who had forged an intellectual and cultural exchange with Tassi—what they collectively called "twinning" of the parks across national boundaries—was especially vocal, penning a note to Berlusconi in hopes of reinstalling Tassi.

While in the immediate aftermath of the scandal Tassi nurtured this resistance, over time its force has waned. It never resulted in any real action that was helpful to Tassi as he fought the charges and conviction. After being the center of attention for so long, first as director and then as the epitome of corruption for prosecutors, he could be forgiven for feeling left behind. And indeed, in the years following his departure from the park, any movement or initiative Tassi began was stopped, and his name was struck from the records of many park documents. Reading the history of the park on its own website, one would have no idea that Tassi had ever existed or that his vision of the park held sway over the environmental movement in Italy. Mentioning him by name to park officials often brings eye rolls or a knowing "Ah, Tassi," uttered with a mix of pity and caution. For those who worked under him, especially those on the lower levels of the organization, his name still creates tension, if not outright anxiety. Their bodies stiffen, and they quickly move the conversation to other topics. Tassi, while remembered adoringly by many in the area, is also something of a curse to those who worked under him and endured his dictums. They are in no hurry to see him valorized as the "father of the Italian park system," as he is called by his admirers.

In part, Tassi's legacy cannot be embraced because doing so could undermine the credibility of the park and its current directors. How can the current park laud a former leader convicted of so many crimes? Further, if the park's story includes its creation by a strong-arm hero, then current directors inevitably appear weak in comparison. So Tassi is easier to dismiss as a criminal than he is to lionize as a groundbreaking conservationist.

Of course, the truth is somewhere in between. Tassi's success came in part from his vision, his passion, and his progressive attempts to change the meaning of nature in Italy. But he implemented his vision by demanding complete and total control and obedience. Those who crossed him were cast aside because dissent was a threat to the inevitable emergence of an illustrious park system.

Tassi's control of the land provided no space for naysayers, and that included not only poachers, loggers, and unlicensed tour operators or hoteliers but also scientists and researchers. Tassi gained a reputation for hunting down people who violated park rules, and indeed he ruthlessly stalked and laid traps for poachers, patiently waiting for them to make a mistake so that he could catch them. The park and its animals, most notably the wolves, flourished because he came down hard on illegal activity. Of all sorts. One needed not be a poacher to feel the long arm of Tassi's law. In one notorious incident, Tassi bulldozed a building that did not have the appropriate permits, reducing it to rubble and fining the contractor. Tassi posed for photos in front of the ruins, a graphic example of his zero-tolerance policy. It helped establish the park as a no-nonsense zone where quibbling and circumventing conservation measures would meet fierce reprisal.

The strict control created problems, though, most notably for those who wanted to help the park preserve rare species, especially the Abruzzo bears. Tassi felt a special calling as protector of the bears, and he strictly limited any interaction with or study of them. Even under pressure from the conservation community to provide clearer evidence of the bears' status, Tassi refused park entry to professors and biologists seeking to help ensure the bears' survival. Over the years of his stewardship, project after project was proposed to Tassi by Italian scientists and researchers, but most met insurmountable resistance, if not outright rejection. If Tassi did not wish it to be, it would not happen. Suspicion began to mount that Tassi was not so much protecting the bears as hiding the fact that the bears were in danger. In whispers, some worried that the bears may already be beyond saving, an unintended and painfully ironic loss to the management practices of one of the bears' greatest admirers and passionate spokespersons.

Paolo Ciucci was among those who attempted to work within the park and who still sometimes faces the lingering suspicion of outside scientists that is one of Tassi's legacies. Ciucci would never have been allowed to conduct all of his work during Tassi's reign, and he laments the years of lost data that Tassi represents. Still, even Ciucci speaks with a degree of admiration for the former director. He recognizes that Tassi was a ceaseless advocate for park wilderness and that his policies may have launched a certain level of nature activism in Italy.

But while Ciucci sees in Tassi a passionate defender of the wild, he also sees the seeds of real harm that would begin to grow like an insidious vine whose tendrils reach into the most remote crevices. Tassi's policies protected the bears, but they also prevented the gathering of important scientific data that might have been used for more extensive preservation campaigns. Because Ciucci began his work just as Tassi was finally forced from his throne, he knows that he has benefitted from fortunate timing. Still, Tassi's influence on the park lingers in the background of Ciucci's science, a reminder of both the good and the bad that comes from the total control Tassi exerted.

The reasons for Tassi's protectionist stance are the subject of endless speculation among those who work on behalf of the park. Certainly, he found ways to financially benefit from his despotism, but no one really doubts his devotion to the park, and some suggest that his barriers against external inquiry should be read as the discretion of a guardian. He kept people out, the reasoning goes, because he understood the precariousness of the bears' situation. He wanted nothing to tip the balance and send the species tumbling into oblivion, and so in an abundance of caution, he essentially quarantined the area, appointed only loyal servants, and treated the park as his possession. From the 1960s until the early 2000s, Tassi stood guard, fending off barbarians who might, even if well-meaning, disrupt the delicate ecological system that allowed the bears to survive.

Such reasoning is not entirely implausible, especially given the sincere regard so many people seem to have for Tassi. But it does not ameliorate the problems the bears now face.

Throughout the 1980s and '90s, scientists and conservationists became alarmed at the lack of verifiable information about the bears, and they started to complain not just to Tassi but also to others within the government and the media. Under increasing pressure to allow scientists into the park to conduct research, Tassi compromised in what could be described as a quintessentially Tassian way. Instead of allowing outside scientists into the park to conduct research, he created his own park-run science group.

Tassi insisted then and continues to insist today that outside scientists had ulterior motives for their work, whether to prop up their own careers or to undermine his reputation. So he argued that the park needed to have loyal park servants—not outsiders—conducting research. He hired his own scientists, and they investigated matters at his behest. If international researchers or nearby scholars wanted to conduct work, they would either work alongside Tassi's hand-selected group, or they would not work at all inside the park. Usually, it was the latter.

The result of the park-run science outfit has been mixed, at least in terms of serving the long-term interests of the park. Tassi's science staff, while usually focused and well-meaning, worked under tight budgets and only on those projects that Tassi found worthwhile or that they could convince him would benefit the park. There were usually only two or three members on staff. Because at any given time there might only be two in-park scientists, the amount of work that could be accomplished was modest. Underfunded, not independent, and working within a notoriously bureaucratic system that emphasized pet projects, the science team under Tassi produced pamphlets and propaganda more than they conducted traditional scientific research, demonstrating it was more a system of vigorous promotion than of systematic discovery and advocacy.

As the years drifted by, the science group at the park collected remarkably little hard data except when pressed to do so. At one point in the 1990s, Tassi faced pressure to come up with a firm number as to the Abruzzo bear population, so he asked his rangers and naturalists to provide him with one. Stories conflict on what sorts of numbers Tassi received, but he would eventually insist that the bears had recovered to at least 100 or 120 individuals. Yet no concrete evidence—no scientific literature or raw data—exists, except a trail of Tassi's claims. There are no hair samples, DNA tests, scat samples, or even standardized written eyewitness reports from rangers or naturalists to support his claim. The truth is, as long as Tassi ran the park, the actual status of the bears remained a mystery, despite his insistence today that they numbered more than 100 when he was forced out.

The bears, in fact, were then and remain now in a profoundly precarious position. The degree of the threat they are under has only become clear because recent scientific investigations have demonstrated in unambiguous terms that disaster looms. Ciucci's work, conducted initially just after Tassi's leadership but mostly over the last decade, suggests that only around 40 bears remain. Among them are, at most, a dozen breeding females who produce litters only once every three years. In any given year, maybe three or four new bears are born, a number that the bear mortality rate matches or, in some years, exceeds.

The bears, in other words, cling to existence.

Ciucci and several other biologists and environmentalists are hell-bent on changing that. To do so, they are trying to overturn decades-long habits within the park, traditions of sequestration and isolation that began under Tassi but have persisted. Ciucci is among those who, despite frustration with Tassi, genuinely believes that he may have single-handedly preserved the bears in the early decades of the park's existence, but Ciucci knows that new threats have emerged that park administration cannot combat alone, and he and his team have attempted to shine a spotlight on the desperate situation in order to gather allies and counter the new threat. They want to demonstrate to the international scientific and environmental communities that these are by any reasonable measure the rarest bears on Earth. They are a remnant, a holdover from another time, essentially a living and breathing fossil—and they are facing an insidious and unexpected threat to their survival.

The new threat relies on invisibility, silence, and shadows. It feasts on inaction, creeping into daily lives without recognition. It grows through a subtle play of power that seems innocuous, if not utterly harmless, and it knows that as long as it stays out of sight, it will grow too large for any single person to stand against it, not even a towering figure like Tassi.

The bears of Abruzzo are under siege by organized crime.

The Mafia wants its land. And it will kill to get it.

# PART IV: BANDITS AND BUREAUCRACY

# 18

~~~~

# Smoke

It usually happens at night. Deep in the forests of southern Italy, a man turns off the main road, shuts off his headlights, and drives a short distance on an obscure side road, coming to a stop in a remote area of a national park. He emerges from his truck, walks to the rear, and grabs a container from the bed of the vehicle. The air is sharp with the smell of gasoline. He moves to the passenger side, opens the door, and removes a small box from the seat. The box shakes, as though alive, and when he opens the lid, a cat pops up its head. It looks at him, then complains. Thick strips of newspaper have been wrapped around its tail, and it demands to be freed from the burden. The man, though, has other plans.

He snatches the animal by its neck and pins it to the ground. He opens the canister of gasoline, and he pours the accelerant on the newspaper, soaking it and the hindquarters of the cat. Then, without a word, he flicks open a lighter, touches its blue flame to the newspaper, and releases the cat into the woods. On some nights, he repeats the process, releasing multiple flaming animals into the dry understory.

The resulting forest fires are usually brief, but they are fatal for the cats and for any other animals in their path. The perpetrators are never found. The cats, burned to death, always are. They are among the mounting casualties in an offensive against the parks launched by a surprising and insidious group, and their deaths represent an escalation of a campaign against park regulations meant to subdue local officials. It's an escalation that spells doom for wildlife if it is not stopped, but it's one for which there is no easy solution. Negotiations with the group would be the obvious way to solve the problem, as would a crackdown on their activities, but the group is immune to normal tactics.

The Italian Mafia is not known to negotiate.

Nor does it tolerate limits on its power.

Under siege by one of the oldest crime syndicates in history, the Italian national parks have virtually no defense against mob activity, and few observers see any viable path to peace short of massive state police intervention. Park officials have little training to combat organized crime and very few resources to dedicate to law enforcement. For years, park rangers have labored under insufficient funding and low morale thanks to the relative lack of significance parks play in the daily lives of Italians. Unlike the American imagination, which, since the first parks were founded, includes space for wilderness and parkland, the Italian does not. Or, if it sometimes might, it certainly does not during times of tremendous socioeconomic crises such as those that have gripped the country since the turn of the millennium. With no training and, for many, no will to fight against an organized offensive, park staff have been unable to counter the insidious effects of mob crime. Some worry that park officials themselves have been infiltrated and are complicit in Mafia activity.

Others besides the Mafia have used burning cats as weapons. Purportedly, a few inspired Italian labor groups, as well as disgruntled farmers whose pension benefits have been cut, have used cats to start forest fires, and they may be the first culprits to resurrect this unsettling form of combat first described in a 1584 German military tome called *The Fire Book*. But the Mafia appears to be using the tactic with increasing precision to target park managers with whom they disagree. When the forest fires do not make the statement strongly enough, though, they turn to more traditional methods of reproach. More traditional and more violent.

While the Mafia in southern Italy has resorted to using flaming cats to make its point, the fight in other parts of Italy has remained, as yet, invisible. Rumors persist that the primary group operating throughout the Abruzzi is the Camorra, the notoriously violent and implacable Naples Mafia. A crime group whose organizational model might best be compared to metastatic cancer, its influence spreads because it has a decentralized power structure. Though the core disease emerged in Naples in the nineteenth century, individual clans have stretched across Italy and operate independently from the Naples core. Like tumors, they grow and destroy life around them. In Abruzzo, the Camorra has set up heroin distribution networks, underwritten illegal businesses, extorted officials, stolen money intended to repair earthquake damage, bribed state officials, poisoned wildlife, and terrorized local citizens with threats of violence.

In 1994, south of Abruzzo in the town of Bari, the Camorra assassinated a priest while he was preparing for mass in the church of St. Nicholas. Don Giuseppe "Peppino" Diana had crusaded against the Camorra, publicly condemning its various criminal activities. He wrote open letters to his parish and testified in hearings. He organized protests and set up centers for refugees escaping mob influence. Though outside the boundaries of the parks in central Italy, he recognized the mob's influence on the land and on the people who would work it, and he rallied people against it. On the March morning of his assassination, a lone gunman entered his church and asked parishioners where he could find Father Diana. He was pointed to a nearby room where the priest was preparing for mass, and, according to Roberto Saviano, who has written extensively about the event, upon entering the room walked up to a man he found there.

He asked him, "Who is Don Diana?" When the man responded "I am," the attacker shot him five times: twice in the head, once in the face, plus one shot each to his arm and hand.

The killing of Diana was as brazen as any Mafia killing in a generation, and his death is still commemorated today. Despite some local papers smearing Diana, declaring him linked to the Camorra and just a casualty of his own transgressions, no evidence ever surfaced to demonstrate such claims. Indeed, his entire life speaks to the opposite.

That in 2010 the town of Barrea, which rises along a crystalline lake on the edge of Abruzzo National Park, hosted a month-long exhibition of Diana and his writings is telling. The title of the exhibition, "Don Peppino Diana: For the Love of My People," referenced Diana's most famous phrase: "For the love of my people, I will not be silent." The statement came at the end of a legendary epistle he wrote condemning the Camorra, and it has become a rallying cry for those who oppose the Mafia. Indeed, the hardly veiled description of the Abruzzo exhibition by one of its organizers makes clear that the exhibition was meant to draw attention to Camorra activities in the region: "The exhibition aims to be a moment of reflection that, with other initiatives planned, fosters life for the Park and Lawfulness program. The Park and Lawfulness program focuses attention on the most non-derogable requirement of honesty and legality at every level." The implicit message, of course, is that honesty and legality may not be working at every level of the park. The exhibition, while certainly a moment of reflection, was a very public statement against Mafia incursions into the area.

The message has not been without reason. Within the last decade, increasing evidence of Mafia activity within and around the park has surfaced, some of it providing startling revelations of just how deeply embedded the Mafia may be within the area. For example, in April of 2007, Italian police discovered the hideout for a central figure of the Naples clan. He sequestered himself in Abruzzo National Park.

In the small village of Opi, Nicola Del Villano hid from federal authorities for more than a decade. From there, he ran the Mafia's empire in the region, managing a portfolio of diverse holdings that included car dealerships, local businesses, and drug-running outfits. At the time of his arrest, he was listed as one of the ten most wanted people in Italy, and he had been on the lam for more than fifteen years, hiding comfortably in an unassuming and picturesque village inside the park.

Labeled one of the most beautiful villages of Italy, Opi is for many the heart of the region, a place where one can witness wolves prancing across the valley just below town or chamois traipsing across the rocky face of Mount Marsicano. From the ancient village walls, one can see Pescasseroli barely five miles to the northwest. For a time, it was also the heart of the Camorra in the Marsi. Del Villano lived in complete secrecy in the town, and even to this day, many people in neighboring towns have no idea that he had called it home. He was not, however, actually arrested in Opi. Instead, Del Villano was detained as he was returning from a run to Naples to consult with his associates and his boss. He had pulled off the main highway from Naples to Rome in the town of Cassino to eat at, of all places, a McDonald's. He never got his order. Cops who had been tailing him decided to act, and they arrested him and searched his vehicle. In it, they found stolen and falsified credit cards and SIM cards. He did not put up a fight.

His apprehension, while a significant success for the Italian authorities, surprised many investigators because, when his hideout was discovered, it demonstrated precisely how deeply the Camorra had become embedded into a relatively obscure hamlet with a population of barely 400 people. The authorities moved swiftly to try to shut down further activity, some of it within Abruzzo National Park. A week after Del Villano was arrested, another member of the Camorra who was wanted on charges of attempted murder was arrested at a campsite in Pescasseroli. Two men who had rented the apartment to Del Villano were also investigated, and charges were levied against them for aiding and abetting the criminal. They were eventually convicted in 2016 of harboring the wanted man and sentenced to two years in prison.

The quick efforts of the police to track down leads associated with Del Villano yielded important results, but they also pointed to more troubling issues with Abruzzo National Park and the areas around it. They suggested that the parks in Abruzzo have not simply served as the hiding places of Camorra fugitives. They illustrated that the Mafia could operate within the parks and could use the parks as part of their operations. Perhaps more troubling, they suggested, at least to some, that the parks may have become significant features of the Camorra's financial empire.

Several types of businesses may have developed roots into the park. Extortion of local businesses is not uncommon, especially at the margins of the park, and construction businesses serve as fronts for government contract theft. In 2011, two apartments and a garage were seized in Pescasseroli by national authorities as illegal properties of a Mafia treasurer, who used them as a way to hide income. Still, the reach of the Camorra into the park is not a subject upon which national officials readily comment. Despite evidence of widespread Camorra activity along the coasts of Abruzzo, and despite evidence of incursions by the so-called "agro-mafia"—which are branches of *mafioso* that exploit agricultural production and distribution—into towns like Avezzano, which serves as a gateway into Abruzzo National Park and the Gran Sasso and Monti della Laga National Park, top officials are hesitant to discuss possible Mafia activity in the area. The unsurprising result is that identifying how and to what degree organized crime functions within the park is difficult to assess. While park officials past and present, including Franco Tassi and the current leadership of Abruzzo National Park, identify the Mafia as a primary mover in certain parks, locals often pursue their daily lives without much more than a whisper about shady dealings or suspicious activity. The businesses that drive the Camorra into and through Abruzzo National Park are so varied as to be virtually invisible to the average citizen, and yet their web traps many of them in unexpected ways. Indeed, the largest impact of organized crime within the park may come from a business so unassuming and so surprising that few, except local citizens who dare not cross the perpetrators, suspect that it has any significant connections to the mob at all. It is a business that operates in plain sight and in full view of everyone, locals and tourists alike. The trail connecting the business to Camorra or other Mafia syndicates is nearly impossible to follow, if it even exists, and the suggestion that the Mafia would have any interest in this particular business seems so crazy and so patently absurd that few have bothered to give it serious consideration. Those who have attempted have been threatened and in some cases nearly lost their lives.

In Italy, the Mafia has taken to cattle ranching.

Its favorite grazing land is the national parks.

# 19

Ambush

On May 19, 2016, Giuseppe Antoci sped along a mountain highway in Sicily. He was heading home after a day spent advocating for greater crackdown on illegal land use in the region, and it was a typical spring day in southern Italy with clear skies, temperatures in the sixties and seventies, and a few scattered clouds. An occasional shower crossed the land.

As he made his way, drizzle collected on the windshield, but by the time he entered Nebrodi National Park, his home, the skies began to clear. The sky, the land, the rising road—all seemed just like any other day, except for one important fact: Antoci, the president of Nebrodi National Park, was not traveling alone. He was escorted by police, protected from threats he never imagined would be part of the job description of an employee of a national park, let alone its president. But now, as the summer of 2016 and high tourist season approached, he was being driven by bodyguards and followed by a police escort, feeling like a stranger in his own land. His car was armored, a measure he thought excessive and unnecessarily dramatic.

Still, he had received death threats, and the venomous personal attacks had grown increasingly worrisome. He was no fool, and after a whole day testifying against abuses in his park, he knew protection was probably warranted even if it seemed absurd to him. It all seemed unreal—the testimony, the threats against him and his family, the bodyguards. It was as though he were part of some other world or some other life.

His car and the police car following him sped into the deepening evening, and, according to an interview with La7 Attualità, Antoci finally began to relax as they approached and then entered the park. He chatted with the driver of his vehicle and the man assigned to guard him, and at times he looked out the window and reflected on the day and on the fact that he had somehow become worthy of police protection. He was on his own turf now, and, only moments from his house, he could—as he would recount in widely broadcast interviews—imagine finally taking a breath and drifting off to sleep.

A jolt of the car startled him. As it had rounded a corner, his vehicle had screeched to a halt. The escort car behind stopped suddenly as well but drifted slightly closer to Antoci's. Antoci leaned forward, looking past the driver and the dashboard, out past the hood of his car to see why they had stopped so suddenly. He saw a fairly common scene in Italy's hills and mountains. In front of the car, rocks and debris were scattered across the road. A rockslide blocked their way.

Rockslides are not unusual in any mountain terrain, but in this part of Italy, loose rocks frequently tumble down and, like miniature avalanches, litter freeways and country roads. Antoci sat back in his seat, annoyed. As he would recount in his interview with La7 Attualità, he exchanged glances with his guards, who seemed frustrated but aware that they would need to get out of the car and clear the road. For a moment, the blockade seemed like an inconvenience. A nuisance.

In fact, it was an ambush.

Shotguns opened fire on Antoci's vehicle, multiple blasts ringing out and rocking the car. Metal sung, and everyone inside the car ducked. Antoci's bodyguard pressed him to the floorboards and pulled a weapon. The driver looked for an escape route, but they were pinned between the rocks in front and the police car behind them.

More shotgun blasts followed, and the guards moved into action, the driver now exiting the car and the police in the trailing vehicle leaping out to exchange fire.

As he noted in multiple news reports and broadcasts, Antoci remembers thinking that he had finally lost his battle for justice. He could smell the gunpowder, and the sound of the shotgun shells unloading into his vehicle rang with such ferocity that he felt certain he was about to die. He thought of his family. He thought of his successes. He thought of his mistakes.

And a bizarre truth crossed his mind—the truth that in 2016 the head of a national park would be targeted and assassinated by henchmen who were, at heart, cowards and thugs. In that moment, none of it made any sense.

But the police were swift, acting on their training and defending Antoci with the kind of devotion reserved for people who fight for a cause. Firing from beside their vehicles, they located the source of the ambush and unloaded their weapons into the woods. They could hear scrambling, then the distinctive sound of someone cocking a shotgun. After another blast rocked Antoci's car, the police fired again into the assailants' hiding place in the brush alongside the road, this time stepping toward it, steadying their weapons and shooting with precision and certainty.

For a moment, the mountains echoed with gunfire, but just as quickly as the attack happened, it seemed to end. The mountain air stilled. Silence gathered. Darkness settled in. Footfalls from the police echoed from the pavement as they inched toward the edge of the woods. One of the officers spoke loudly into the wilderness, ordering anyone who could hear to drop their weapons and come out, but the officers heard only silence and the distant scuttling of feet on leaves and gravel. One of the other officers poked his head into Antoci's car and inquired after his safety. When he heard Antoci's voice, he knew that the park president had been saved. The assassination attempt had failed.

None of the officers had been injured. At least one of the attackers apparently had. Officials found blood on the roadway and on the forest floor. They also found two Molotov cocktails prepped and ready to light. The ambushers, the police postulated, had planned to burn Antoci's body inside his car to destroy evidence of the attack. The burning would have been a gruesome demonstration of their power and would have sent an unmistakable statement to other park officials: The Mafia controls the park.

The Italians call them *bandits*. For most Americans, the word *bandit* is an old-timey term that has certain degree of absurdity or humor to it. It conjures images of the Old West or melodramatic silent films. One pictures a villain with a black hat, a six-shooter, and a bandanna wrapped around the nose and mouth. There are no "bandits" in America anymore. In Italy, though, the term has force and currency. It is spoken with seething disgust and is used to refer to especially reprehensible criminals—not necessarily the most lawless kind but those who insinuate themselves into daily life and undermine social stability. They represent a special order of lawbreakers who are loathed and often also feared. They are usually synonymous with the mob.

Bandits are undermining the park system throughout Italy. The allegiances of those bandits vary by region, but from Abruzzo over to Lazio and down to Sicily, the Mafia appears to be exploiting gaps in park governance to make money. The full extent of this exploitation is anyone's guess—part of the reason is the slipperiness of Mafia activities; another part of it is lack of certainty about which bandits are genuinely Mafia and which ones may just be exploiting such an association to their favor. Just because criminals are usurping land in a park does not mean they are de facto linked to larger Mafia outfits.

Still, Mafia involvement in Italian parks is direct and demonstrable. No evidence makes this more clear than the brazen assassination attempt on Giuseppe Antoci. The blockade and ambush just miles from Antoci's home deep in the heart of his park suggests the depth of the Mafia's reach and its willingness to terrorize anyone who tries to stop it. Yet it also illustrates the Mafia's increasing desperation to maintain control. Antoci's campaign against exploitation of the land has been successful, and he clearly hit a nerve when some of his policies took hold and led to direct financial losses for organized crime. The attempt to murder him, no matter how troubling, also suggests that his work was succeeding. Such truth, though, is hardly consolation to a man under fire.

Over the last dozen years, Antoci has led an attempt to wrest land from Mafia control in Sicily. In Sicily, the Mafia is the legendary Cosa Nostra, which emerged from a series of family associations that, though initially informal, morphed into ritualistically bound alliances. It remains a confederation of clans. Despite several major crackdowns over the last century, the Cosa Nostra has proved to be remarkably resilient, and various clans have insinuated themselves into just about every line of business, whether illegal or legal. Gambling, drug running, the weapons trade, and prostitution have all been part of the Mafia portfolio, as have laundromats, car dealerships, butcher shops, and many other legitimate businesses that, in one form or another, are under control of Cosa Nostra bosses.

The Cosa Nostra's forays into politics have also been successful over the years, leading to corruption and often invisible deals to heighten the value of Sicilian crime assets. Purportedly, the Cosa Nostra even secured a deal with Silvio Berlusconi, the unapologetic self-proclaimed "best leader in Europe and in the world." The Sicilian Mafia, thanks to its profitability and ability to find seams in laws, as well as its willingness to use violence to secure its ends, has proven impossible to completely root out of the country.

Like any flexible organization whose sole purpose is to enrich itself, the Mafia continually reinvents itself. The Cosa Nostra seems especially adept at developing new funding channels, and in recent years, it has found surprising new approaches to its empire. Since the late 1990s and early 2000s, the Sicilian Mafia has developed elaborate schemes to gorge on international agricultural and environmental subsidies. Using ranchers, shepherds, and government officials, the Mafia has discovered that beef production in particular yields strong returns—remarkably strong returns, with estimates ranging in the tens of millions of dollars. By some reports, this has outstripped profits from drug running and extortion.

The exploitation of loopholes in land-use laws is the centerpiece of new Mafia initiatives, and national parks have become the battleground for the Mafia's profitable foray into farming and ranching. In Sicily, ground zero is Nebrodi National Park, but the Mafia has found itself in battle with an unlikely adversary. As he has noted in several interviews, Giuseppe Antoci never imagined himself a soldier in the war against organized crime. He was simply pursuing his career when he landed in the middle of a park that few others had any desire to manage.

Founded in 1993, Nebrodi National Park is one of the least visited parks in all of Italy. Part of that is its relative isolation, but part of it is its lack of development. Vast swaths of the park are without roads. Villages in the area date as far back as the fourth century, many essentially abandoned today. Part mountain terrain and part open plain and valley, the park boasts impressive views of Sicily's most famous mountain, Mount Etna, a volcano that remains active today. Though not within the Nebrodi park boundaries, Etna dominates the scenery from many parts of the park.

The isolation of the park provides for almost unparalleled solitary walks and trekking in Italy. It also provides opportunity for exploitation. Many Italians are unaware of the park's existence, and its relative lack of tourism only exacerbates the possibility for abuses. If not for the efforts of Antoci, those abuses would, in fact, have never been known.

Antoci has revealed to Sicilians and the rest of Italy precisely how organized crime has infiltrated public lands. He began by holding meetings with a wide array of stakeholders in the area, from local citizens and landowners to public officials. He then investigated precisely how land was being licensed and used in the area, documenting land agreements and tracking land subsidies. He discovered an extensive and systematic swindle. By falsifying documents through an elaborate process of ownership certifications, the Mafia essentially skimmed European Union and Italian subsidies for pasture land inside the park. Total profits from the scheme over the years are impossible to estimate because before Antoci, no attempt to understand the elaborate scheme was ever made. But, if a single year's take was north of €80 million, as the estimates suggest, it is clear that Mafia revenue from livestock and land abuse has topped hundreds of millions of euros. Antoci revealed a very lucrative, but formerly invisible, revenue stream for the Cosa Nostra.

To break this system of land abuse, Antoci developed a plan to combat it. Some now call it the "Antoci Protocol" in recognition of its creator's innovation. It requires stricter examination of ownership and more deeply vetted certification of land use to ensure that land is not owned or operated by the Mafia. It also provides for greater communication between the park and local communities to provide residents who are looking for a way to escape the grip of the Cosa Nostra to share their stories with park and police officials. The protocol has been such a success that officials in Calabria, home to its own special brand of Mafia, the 'Ndrangheta, have imported it to deploy in their province.

As Antoci exposed increasing levels of corruption, he also infuriated crime bosses. They responded first with a smear campaign. In an attempt to undermine his credibility, they sent letters and spread word among local communities that he was the enemy. When that did not work, they responded with violence.

In the summer of 2015, a Molotov cocktail was left for him at a picnic area in the heart of the park, along with a note threatening his life. A few months later, letters containing even more detailed threats and stuffed with bullets were sent to Antoci and the local police, only to be followed by the assassination attempt in the mountains of his own park. Yet Antoci has not been cowed. In an interview covered by multiple media outlets immediately following the attack on his vehicle and escort, he spoke with measured tones: "I know who wants me dead … My commitment does not stop. I'll push forward."

Such commitment comes with a cost. Antoci is under constant protection now, and despite his ongoing campaign to stop organized crime in his park and local communities, the Mafia continues to strike back. The tactic of setting cats on fire and releasing them into the park is only one way they have tried to shut him and his movement down. On Christmas in 2016, they burned down an information center at the entrance to a park village. "A vile Christmas gift," Antoci said in a press briefing in front of the smoldering site. "But we will press forward."

The ultimate outcome of Antoci's battle against the Mafia is far from certain. His successes, however, suggest that with enough dedication, persistence, and leadership, corruption and abuse of public lands can be eliminated from specific areas. Whether it can, in fact, expand and encompass the entirety of the national park system remains to be seen. It takes, in part, a fearless leader willing to press an agenda, but it also takes investigation from other parks and, if Mafia activity is uncovered, acknowledging the problem. Even the act of acknowledgment takes courage, let alone launching a crusade like Antoci's, but as long as the problem is unacknowledged, change is impossible.

The reach of the Mafia into the parks across Italy is unclear. Certainly, the story of Mafia land exploitation in Sicily shocks even many Italians, whose visions of organized crime center on drugs, weapons, prostitution, and extortion. Park abuse seems almost an absurdity. Yet the attack on Antoci in 2016 has driven home the point that great sums of money are at stake in land exploitation, as are the rights of citizens to benefit from legal uses of the land. For Europeans and, indeed, conservationists around the world, Mafia activities in Sicily stand as a warning sign that the forces marshaled against land protection may be more complex and well organized than anyone might have imagined. If the Cosa Nostra's incursions are simply a sign of more widespread exploitation, then Italy, if not other parts of Europe, is up against more than just cultural resistance to change. It is up against criminals who advance their agenda by any means necessary, including assassinations.

The fact that the "Antoci Protocol" has been imported into Calabria suggests that the problems in Sicily are not isolated to that island or the Cosa Nostra, and it raises the question: How far into the Italian parks have various *mafioso* pushed, and which gangs and clans are engaged in the same sorts of activities that have led to the violence in Sicily? Not everyone is convinced that the activity extends outside of the south of Italy. Arrests of members of the Camorra in Abruzzo are not enough to demonstrate that the province is facing the same sort of land exploitation enacted by the Cosa Nostra that Antoci uncovered in Sicily.

Yet Abruzzo is only a few hours north of Calabria, and Naples, the home of the Camorra, is even closer. If Sicilian and Calabrian bosses profit from what is now being called "eco-mafia," the Camorra would not ignore it. Indeed, with footholds much deeper into central and northern Italy, the Camorra would have access to much larger swaths of land. And Abruzzo, despite its proximity to the capital of the country, has little money and even fewer people equipped to resist organized crime, whether it is publicly acknowledged or not.

Widespread agreement exists among many park officials that some bandits, whether Camorra or not, are responsible for the livestock incursions into the park. Even though there have been no prosecutions for illegal livestock activity in Abruzzo National Park, arrests within the park for other offenses over the last decade point rather clearly to Camorra activity in the region, and some residents worry that other discoveries—such as a weapons raid at the park's boundaries that netted a hoard of illegal weapons and more than 2,500 rounds of ammunition—signal a more extensive presence. The 2016 weapons raid followed a report of poaching, and after the arsenal was uncovered, officials immediately sought four local residents responsible for the stash. However, without prosecution, and, more important, without definitive evidence like the kind that Antoci's protocol uncovered in Nebrodi National Park, Mafia involvement in Abruzzo National Park will remain rumor or myth.

It may be that the idea of the Mafia is a convenient excuse for park officials' failure to protect the land. Park rangers and management are simply not designed to combat organized crime. As such, the idea of the Mafia provides a useful excuse for apathy or, perhaps more precisely said, lack of systematic change. Few people will blame park officials for not stopping cattle grazing if doing so comes at the risk of their own lives. A few extra cows in the park seems a small price to pay for avoiding conflict with the mob.

It may also be that the term *mafia*, like the term *bandit*, has come to be so widely applied that it represents any criminal working against Italian authorities. Residents may label any suspicious activity as mob related simply because it appears to be organized and deliberate. If it's bad, it's *mafia*, in the same way that in mid-twentieth-century America, the label *communist* was used to describe any suspicious person or activity.

So, for now, Mafia activity in Abruzzo National Park remains invisible, the stuff of rumors and innuendos. And yet, ask many park officials, local citizens, and not-for-profit environmental groups in the area, and they are unequivocal: Organized crime operates in the Abruzzi. For them, a one-sided war between the Abruzzo parks and ungovernable bandits has begun, and the parks are losing.

# 20

*Uso Civico*

If the Mafia is good at anything, it is hiding in plain sight. It does so by exploiting systems that function to benefit communities but that have gaps in their operations. The systems that make a community work, things like sanitation and road construction and all manner of government agencies, were created with public users in mind. They were not created to avoid Mafia corruption. They were created to function smoothly, not to avoid perversion by nefarious actors.

Criminal organizations like the Mafia locate seams where profits can be turned at the expense of others, and they maximize revenue by threatening anyone who attempts to close the gaps. Legislative bureaucracy, the bane of any citizen's existence, is actually built on attempts to cover holes in laws in order to shut down people who exploit unintended consequences of otherwise well-meaning mandates. As one seam is stitched closed, however, another pops open further down the line. Criminals are willing to follow the fissures no matter how small or where they may lead, and they find opportunities in surprising places. In Italy, the Mafia, chasing money and power, has found both in parks and cows.

In other countries, especially the US, the idea that cattle can be lawlessly grazed in a national park seems absurd. Imagine driving into Yosemite and seeing a massive herd of Hereford plucking lichen from the base of Half Dome, or picture a gathering of Charolais sipping at the waters of Old Faithful, and the oddness of it comes into focus. For most Americans, parks represent wilderness, a place for native flora and fauna. In Italy, however, the line between public land and private is less clear. What is and is not admissible under law is murky, and generations of local codes—some written, some not—cloud any attempt to see ahead clearly. This is especially true with the parks.

Despite being national parks, Abruzzo National Park and its neighboring preserves are effectively managed by the province of Abruzzo. While federal laws provide guidance on land management, and while certain federal mandates establish policy, regional politics and funding dictate most of what happens on a daily basis in the park. While this is empowering to the province because it provides for more local control, more efficient oversight, and, in theory, more employment opportunities for area residents, it also means that park management is subject to the whims of provincial governments. And local officials.

Each park in Abruzzo has several administrators. The most important in terms of the day-to-day operations is the park director, who is appointed for three- to five-year terms by a governing body that oversees parkland use. Park directors are often science professionals, naturalists, or professionals with administrative experience. Most have pursued careers outside of the parks before moving into park administration.

Above the director is the park president, who is often quite distanced from the daily management of the park, but he (pretty much always "he") can have tremendous power. While the park director manages the budget and develops fiduciary plans, the president ultimately holds the purse strings, serving as an overseer of the public interest as well as the public face of the park. In this system, a park president is supposed to act as a kind of check on the power of the director, a person who can keep big-picture issues in mind, represent the public interest, align the park with federal guidelines, and ensure appropriate use of public funds. It is a system that aims to maintain accountability and to develop public trust, but one key feature of the appointment of a park president undermines any purported benefit the system might have. In Italy, the park president is a political appointee, sometimes renewed on a yearly basis.

Park presidencies currently are distributed as political favors by ruling parties. Accountants, architects, retirees, local business owners, wealthy donors—all have served as park presidents despite having no background in park management, ecology, biology, sustainability, environmental law, natural history, or any number of more appropriate backgrounds for overseeing a national park. In the US, such appointments seem outrageous. But in the Italian system, and among an Italian public that has demonstrated little will to investigate or change the system, such appointments are a fact of park management, and they encourage deeply problematic relationships to emerge. Perhaps more important, they also prevent systematic and enduring oversight from occurring. Even if a particularly valuable president is appointed, the political nature of the appointment guarantees lack of continuity and prevents lasting change in the parks. It also ensures that the management of the lands is a hot potato that no one can hold without being burned.

The political appointee system essentially ties the hands of the park director. Saddled with daily management issues and strapped for cash yet beholden to the wishes of the president, the director usually spends most of his career treading water. While he may have leeway to launch initiatives to, say, balance a budget or reorganize chains of command, he is often unable to develop long-term solutions for the most pressing issues of the park. Even if he is able to do so under one president, an incoming president may have completely different priorities, ones connected to the political environment that saw him secure his post. So the director has very little incentive to make long-term plans. Why should he, when those plans might be unceremoniously undone when the political winds blow in a new direction?

No less important is that the park director often faces pressure to respond to threats to a park yet has few resources to dedicate to them. Even if a park president and a park director agree on what may be the most pressing issues of the park—something that is hardly guaranteed—budgets for the parks are tight, and responding to new situations means reallocation of funds that is sometimes difficult for directors to justify to their overseer. Accordingly, directors are often unable to mount any meaningful defense against attacks on the parks, whether they be political, environmental, or criminal.

For Abruzzo National Park, one of those attacks is the incursion of livestock into the park. It is a political, cultural, and likely criminal problem that exploits centuries-old traditions and legal precedent in order to undermine park autonomy. At the heart of the issue is the idea of *uso civico*. Translated as "civic use," the concept has wide applicability in Italy. The idea derives in part from the ancient idea of Lex Agraria, a Roman statute that allowed plebeians to harvest wild animals and small amounts of lumber from land owned by nobles. Though it was wildly popular with the poor in Roman times, the ruling class loathed it, and it led to the assassination of one of its proponents. The spirit of that law, however, has persisted.

To this day, Italian law allows limited private use of public lands. Indeed, not just public lands, but other people's private land as well. Think of it as a mandate to act neighborly even if you have no desire to do so. Under the law, if a person needs, for instance, some firewood to keep warm in the winter, he can go into parkland or another person's private property and take a tree or two for wood. Or, if he is hungry, he can take a boar or a deer from nearby land, whether his or not, to feed his family. Similarly, he might, if he has no property himself, be able to set up a small garden to grow vegetables. Such little gardens exist throughout many Italian parks, and in Abruzzo, they can be found in some of the high mountain valleys or on the boundaries of the park where, because of the law, little energy is given to policing the extent of the private use of the land.

The *uso civico*, when paired with the political appointment of presidents, creates a vulnerability that some locals have exploited, typically on a small scale that, when taken in isolation, presents minimal problems for the park. Park directors and rangers often turn a blind eye, knowing there is little to be gained from enforcing park policies over and against millennia-old traditions of subsistence farming, even if some do take it beyond subsistence and turn a small profit from it. Yet the lax patrolling of *uso civico* has opened the door for more organized exploitation of the land.

The *uso civico* was intended to allow families to survive when they could not themselves afford to buy land on which to raise crops or maintain livestock. It provided the lower classes with an opportunity to own small herds of sheep or cattle without having to endure the costs of land ownership. While the tradition remains and some families still keep a few animals with which to feed themselves, others have grown their herds, which now number in the hundreds or thousands of head. Such herds require broad pastures and rich fields on which to graze, and the parks provide both. Perhaps more important, especially to those who purportedly underwrite the livestock maintenance, the parks provide free pasture.

In Abruzzo, as in Sicily and Calabria, the Lex Agraria tradition has created one of those seams in the law that the Mafia can exploit. Cattle roam the parks because their owners lay claim to the public land as their right, and even if some pay nominal leasing fees—and few, if any, do—the profits to be made far outstrip any expense, especially if the ranchers are themselves being underwritten by other interests. In Abruzzo, the rumors persist, those underwriters are the Neapolitan mob. With deep wallets and even deeper savvy in negotiating gaps in the law, the Camorra, according to many in the area, has taken to livestock herding. The result has been devastating for the land and its wildlife.

Especially Abruzzo's bears.

# 21

~~~

# Fade Out

Herds of cows congregate daily along the main road in Abruzzo National Park. Visible from virtually any approach into the park, they gather and feed on the lush greenery of the Sangro Valley. The most popular entrance into the park is along State Route 83, also known as the Marsicana Highway, a road that twists and turns along an escarpment while it climbs into the hamlet of Gioia Vecchio. The village is a hub for bear watching. On weekends in the summer, hundreds of tourists flock to it, binoculars in hand, and gather on a shaded promontory that overlooks a valley, craning their necks hoping for a glimpse of a bear. They often see one. Scrambling up a hill or tipping rocks and boulders in search of ants, bears cross the area almost daily within full view of onlookers.

Perched on the side of a mountain, Gioia Vecchio once boasted nearly 5,000 citizens, but an earthquake in the early twentieth century leveled nearly every building in it, and the townspeople abandoned it. Most resettled in the valley toward Avezzano, where, under stewardship of the government, a new city, Gioia dei Marsi, was founded. The new municipality, now with about 2,000 people, maintains oversight of Gioia Vecchio even though barely a dozen buildings remain from before the earthquake. On a crowded day, about a dozen citizens call it home.

Just as the main road leaves Gioia Vecchio and turns into the heart of the park, the landscape opens into a long view toward Mount Marsicano. The mountain is flanked by broad verdant valleys, and on either side of the Marsicana Highway, high ridges and towering peaks rise like sentinels. Cattle graze both sides of the road, feeding from sunrise to sunset on a luxurious mixture of greens. Cowbells clang, audible from every overlook above the valley, and the occasional moo echoes from crag to canyon.

One of the last buildings as the road drops out of Gioia Vecchio is a cattle rancher's abode, and cows often mass up against a pen of mud and rock, waiting for feed or attention or both. The unmistakable smell of a cattle herd greets any visitor within moments of first entering the park.

The long, high valley that drops down out of Gioia Vecchio is prime grazing land. The cows, a light gray or white breed called Marchigiana, are kept throughout Abruzzo, with some animals having almost blue tinges to them. They lumber slowly up and down the green hillsides, and their bells, echoing with crisp tones in the high altitude, can be heard for miles on a clear, dry day. They not infrequently nuzzle their way past barbed wire fences to wander the roadsides, snacking on mountain pansy or clover and roundly ignoring honks or shouts from drivers. They also amble into Gioia Vecchio itself, looking a bit befuddled, if also unconcerned, as they mill among the last remaining buildings. A cow or two standing stock-still at the doorway to the village's San Vincenzo Church makes for a remarkable photo. The animals' owner seems decidedly unconcerned about their wanderings.

The valley was once forest, and the mountains persist in trying to return it to woodland. Mounds of head-high shrubs pack the landscape, the vanguard of new tree growth. Before they mature, however, most saplings will be mowed down to ensure that pastureland triumphs. On the high ridges, clear-cuts of forest remain open. Wind batters the mountains and scatters topsoil. The remaining thin soil is hard to replace, and once deep-rooted trees are gone, young trees cannot gain a foothold. In the valley, though, the soil is thick, and hillsides protect young forests from ravaging winds. Streams nourish fresh growth, and some trees may grow a foot or more a year. The trees thrive, but so, too, do the cows. As do the cattle ranchers.

Cattle have grazed parts of Abruzzo for generations, and it has been common for local families to maintain a couple of cows for milk. For a time, the Italian Red Pied cow was abundant, but other breeds have overtaken the local herds, with the Marchigiana dominating the livestock roaming the park. Before either, though, a local Abruzzo cow lived throughout the region and provided sustenance for local farmers and villages. The Podolica Abruzzese di Montagna is now extinct, lost to history and lost to the demands of beef production. The Marchigiana has taken its place. A more productive beef breed, it offers dramatic upscaling of meat processing and broader possibilities for exporting outside of the region. Breeders have improved upon the animals, shaping their bodies and their beef to fit the needs of the market. The result has been larger herds with deeper incursions into the parks to sustain them.

The native Abruzzese breed did not graze in the high valleys of what is now Abruzzo National Park, or if it did, it did not do so in large numbers. The high altitudes of the park were the domain of sheep, and cows, the relatively few that lived in the park, stuck to the valleys. Beef markets were not as well developed, either, so an invisible economic cap kept herds small. Indeed, for the most part, the Abruzzese cows were domestic providers whose numbers rarely exceeded a few dozen head at most. Many families kept just a couple of individuals for their own use. They were hardly the cow to populate massive herds. Further, they were better adapted to the valleys of Abruzzo, where forests reclaimed land with such speed that local farmers could hardly keep up with maintaining broad pastureland. Small acreage could be managed by families, but vast acreage was an impossible task for a small clan of people. Tree growth in cow pasture made the prospect of ongoing land maintenance hardly worth the effort of owning and managing a beef herd. Mechanization of farm machinery and the new breeds of cow, however, changed that. The family cow lapsed into extinction, and the beef herd, supported by tractors and chainsaws, took its place.

The establishment of Abruzzo National Park aimed to protect land from overuse and exploitation. While its creation was not aimed at absolutely prohibiting some cattle grazing, Italian policy prevented larger herds from entering the park. It certainly prevented extensive landscape change to accommodate the domesticated animals, sheep notwithstanding. The collapse of the Italian economy, however, has radically changed the ability—and the will—of park officials to manage the land for public use, and cattle ranchers, many of whom come from southern Italy and are not original residents of Abruzzo, have taken control of important sections of the park. Their operations, while hardly the model of efficiency of the massive ranching in the western United States or Texas, are remarkably well established and financially supported. They operate throughout the park systems in Italy, but in Abruzzo, they have made one of the Abruzzo National Park's most important valleys their home.

The valley extending from Gioia Vecchio to Pescasseroli is legendary for wildlife viewing. On virtually any day, a deer, a boar, a wolf, or a bear may be visible from the road. In the height of summer, cars poke along, their passengers scanning hill and vale for wild animals. They are frequently rewarded. A deer might graze alongside a boar, whose snout and tusks plow through the rich earth and toss clumps of grass and rock into the air. A pack of wolves might cross the road, darting across the asphalt before slowing and glancing back at the cars. Bears sometimes roll around on a copse and stare down at the congregation of tourists below, many of whom, with cameras and telescopic lenses, snap such a swift succession of photos that the air fills with clicks. The animals gather in this valley rich with forage to rollick in the morning and bed down at night, but they are no longer alone. The cows, and their handlers with their machines, crowd the scene.

Unlike the shepherds, whose long history of connection to the land was a point of pride, the new ranchers seem only vaguely interested in the value of the land as home to diverse and novel wildlife. Certainly, their underwriters share no sense of obligation to local economies, nor do they seem to have any sense that the land, once beech forest, belongs to the public or to the animals that have called the region home for a millennium. Their interests are not with the park but with profit, and they graze the land to support a larger industry.

More important, they do not tolerate anyone or anything that interrupts their work. They have no interest in having their industry curtailed, and they have zero patience for disruption, whether by park rangers who might limit their grazing, wildlife that might undermine the integrity of pastureland, or local shepherds who might romanticize days of vast sheep herds. They have no tolerance for boars that scare the cows, or deer that graze on the grasses that cows could feed on, or wolves that might take a calf.

And they most certainly do not tolerate the bears, whose claim to the precious parcel of land now called the Abruzzo National Park predates cow grazing by a thousand years.

The kindly bears of Abruzzo are, in the simplest terms, a threat to a thriving beef industry in the park. The bears are beloved around much of Italy, more beloved than Abruzzo National Park itself and certainly more beloved than the Camorra or any organized crime syndicate. Yet the bears cannot be tolerated because they, as symbols of cooperation between man and beast and as testament to the value of ancient traditions, have the power to unite citizens and end the occupation of the land. The more visible the bears become, the more dangerous they are. If Italians forget that they have national parks or they ignore the importance of wilderness, they need only be reminded of the bears, and they come together to take a stand. The ranchers know this, so they wage a quiet war, doing damage to the bears in ways that are unlikely to cause a stir and unlikely to rally defenders of the park.

While in the south of Italy, organized crime wages a direct war, whether through brazen shootouts or through arson, in Abruzzo, a cold war rages. Silent and insidious, the criminals hide under statutes like the *uso civico* to take more and more land for themselves. From the roadside, tree harvesters can be seen clearing forests in the light of day, and new fences appear to cordon off for cows what were once hidden glens and refuges for wild animals. Illegal slaughterhouses pop up in old storage barns, and streams, once protected by buffers of brush and native grasses, are opened as watering troughs for livestock, who mill about in their waters defecating and polluting them. Through a patient and gradual encroachment over a period of years, if not decades, the cows slowly take the land from the bears. And the bears, with fewer and fewer passageways to call their own, hide or leave.

They wander away from the safety of the park, leaving behind the once prime habitat in order to scavenge in buffer zones and village boundaries. They drift from the valleys that now are home to herds of cows and sequester themselves in the dwindling ancient forests far from the Abruzzese, the people who have known them and lived with them for generations. With their isolation, the bears' story is increasingly forgotten by a people who once found in them a symbol of strength and perseverance. The relationship between bears and the local people, once intimate, is now distant, in time and in space, and the bears transform from a source of pride to just another headache, just another hurdle to the progress of a region.

The bears, in other words, simply disappear.

And no one—except those who dream of their destruction—will realize it before it is too late.

# 22

Pax Romana and
the "Nature Tax"

In over a thousand years of recorded history, no record exists of an Apennine brown bear attacking a human. A millennium of peaceful cohabitation. In the lore of large-animal and human coexistence, there is no comparable record of side-by-side living. The Abruzzo bear is unlike any other bear out there.

While Bruno; his mother, Jurka; Daniza; and their Slovenian ancestors and siblings romp through northern Italy with sometimes violent abandon, Abruzzo bears breeze through forests like friendly ghosts or harmless hermits. Most locals love the Abruzzo bear, sometimes calling him "father bear" in doting, lilting Italian. While a healthy skepticism and sometimes fear of the bears remains in the mountains of Abruzzo, most know the bears to be peaceful, reclusive, and downright friendly. They have formed a relationship with the bears that other parts of the world would hardly believe. Indeed, the relationship between the so-called Italian grizzlies and the Abruzzese is a modern Pax Romana and a model of cohabitation, if not symbiosis. Bears and humans have found a way not only to live together but also to share resources.

How that relationship developed has been lost to history, but traces of it remain in local stories and in the land itself, where human activity has left records that can be seen from the roads crisscrossing the region. Across Abruzzo, mountaintops are barren of trees. While in some cases, the open alpine landscape is the result of elevation, many other cases are, in fact, man-made, alpine-like creations. They are stunningly beautiful, even if they are artificial. From the valleys, they appear to be great fields of green that roll over the tops of the mountains. Deer graze in them, and wild boars scurry across the open expanses, stopping occasionally to root around and tear up the vegetation, exposing black earth and white limestone. From the mountaintops and barren ridges themselves, the views stretch on a clear day for a hundred miles up and down the Apennines, with the Adriatic visible to the east from some of the peaks. The open expanses provide some of the most accessible and scenic hikes in Europe, and it seems for all the world that it is true alpine habitat.

It is not. While some of the mountains in the region climb above 9,000 feet and have the signature barren look of the Italian Alps to the north, most of the open land in Abruzzo National Park comprises man-made pastures. Cleared generations ago for sheep, the land has been grazed for so long that much of it has essentially transformed into a false alpine region, complete with some of the same flora and fauna that exist in higher elevations. While great forests thrive across the region, stretches of barren land wind through and above them, testaments to human need and consumption.

Precisely when and how the area became home to sheep herding is subject to speculation among local storytellers. The tales are a local pastime, but what is clear is that shepherds had no illusions about the wildness of their region and the costs of doing business in it. Families throughout the region report that previous generations spoke openly about sharing the land with the bears. And the bears, apparently, learned to share the land with the shepherds as well.

Among some of the Abruzzese, the notion of the "nature tax"

emerged, and local families still mention the term with a kind of wistful nostalgia. The idea was that one had to pay nature for the privilege of working the land. Of course, one only pays taxes up the hierarchical chain to those who have dominion over the land, and in this case, the king of the natural world was unequivocally the brown bear. At some point in the history of sheep herding, shepherds decided to work with, instead of against, the bears. Instead of constantly worrying about whether the bears would take a sheep, they included a couple of extra sheep in the herd with the knowledge that at some point, the bears (or perhaps the wolves) would need to be paid. This tax, however, extended beyond payment with lambs or sheep. Some locals would plant an extra apple tree a bit farther away from the rest or would set up an extra beehive in the apiary, knowing full well that occasionally a bear would come and have a hankering for some sweet treats.

The bears, apparently, rather agreed with this arrangement. No one can recall an encounter with an aggressive bear, and the official storyline, borne out by the complete lack of mention of bear attacks in standard historical documents, is that the bears have never mauled a human. Certainly, there have been no fatal encounters. One park official, speaking on condition of anonymity, admitted that at least one person had been injured by a bear, but that person had shot the bear, failed to kill it, and approached the animal to finish the job. The bear, not keen on being slain by hand, fought back. "The guy deserved it," the park official said, and few would likely consider such an encounter a "bear attack."

Of course, this is not to say that shepherds were not aggravated by the bears. Some certainly must have been, and some must certainly have feared stumbling into one in the high meadows. Still, they had taken other precautions to ensure they and their flocks were safe and that their homesteads were not ravaged by hungry bears. Livestock pens provided a measure of deterrence, especially for shy bears, but the presence of *cane da Pastore Maremmano Abruzzese*, a sheepdog native to Abruzzo, provided the best protection from bears. Maremma Sheepdogs are notoriously independent and rugged yet remarkably gentle. They are large and look like an albino Newfoundland or a pure-white Pyrenean Mountain Dog. Able to make long traverses with their herds, today they frolic across the valleys and mountaintops of Abruzzo, apparently free of their guard duties. They are by reputation fearless and willful, devoted to their owners and, above all else, their herds.

This native dog stands as the great guardian of the region, and his distinctive role in shaping the cultural history of the area should be seen as just as important as the role of the bears in shaping the identity of the region. They are ubiquitous, they are unmistakable, and they are, after a good wash of their thick coat, perfectly charming. Italians, betraying their ongoing pride in regional history, insist that Maremmas raised in one valley are distinct from those in the neighboring valley or from the neighboring hilltop town. Each little corner of Abruzzo, locals insist, has its own breed of Maremma, perfectly adapted to that spot in the mountains.

The breed purportedly extends back to Roman times and has been a crucial part of the Pax Romana between animal and human in central Italy. Generations of shepherds have lived peacefully with the bears and wolves, knowing that some small portion of their herds may be lost to scavenging beasts but that the rest were well protected by the loyal Maremmas. The result? Not just peace but also pride.

The Abruzzese tout their relationship with the land and animals as central to their character. They have reached a delicate balance, one whose foundation is respect for the power of the bears and wolves in the area even while they demand their own respect. The Maremmas represent this desire for respect, even if it also represents the truce struck between man and beast. It represents human adaptation to nature, a willingness to accommodate, even if only to a certain degree.

The dog embodies a long-standing peace, forged over generations and paid for by offerings of goodwill, and it represents long-standing pride in what is possible if humans work with animals and not against them. They represent balance, even if a tentative one, and their pervasiveness is a sign of health in the region.

Yet today the Maremmas are declining in Abruzzo.

And they are seen with increasing frequency wandering village alleys and valley byways instead of the mountainsides and high grazing lands. They tend to smaller flocks, fewer sheep, and come down from the mountains to lounge on street curbs and scavenge for food in trash bins. On any given night, a vagrant pup might play in Pescasseroli's central square, chewing a crackling plastic bottle it plucked from roadside waste.

They are restless, and they are signaling to anyone who will listen that the delicate balance between man and beast has been tipped in favor of man.

They are telling us that the great peace has finally come to an end.

# 23

## The Cows of Little Tibet

No one wants to be head of Abruzzo National Park if the Abruzzo bears pass into history. This fact ensures that the park president and the park director remain vigilant, but it does not necessarily equip them to combat threats to the bears, especially organized criminal activity. It requires them to address each and every bear death, to run autopsies and issue reports on their findings. It requires them to send rangers to track the bears, to photograph and record them, and to confiscate any bear hazard, whether poison bait or poaching rifles. It requires them to mount ongoing public education campaigns. It requires all of this and more, yet they must do so with very little funding and with an eye to the possibility that the people they face down are not opportunistic criminals but metastatic growths of a cancer that, as yet, Italy has been unable to cure.

The process for installing new park directors, while not as explicitly political as park presidencies, nonetheless is highly politicized. Directors are nominated from the region in which the park is situated. Three nominees are sent up to the Ministry for the Environment, Land and Sea, and the minister then makes his selection.

Those on the outside of the process complain that park directors are just rotated from park to park, switching places in order to allow them to maintain control of the park system. The same names appear year in and year out, and when one leaves a park, he is simply moved to another. New blood is rare, and when it does enter the pool of candidates, it remains circulating with the others, mixed in and integrated into the system. Change—real change through fresh perspectives or progressive thinking—is rare. Perhaps more important, corruption thrives. Within a closed system, highly controlled by a core group of individuals, the potential for nepotism and other forms of corruption emerges with increasing force each year. In closed systems, where appointments are made without transparency, insidious actors can have remarkable influence.

They do not give that influence away without a fight.

Dario Febbo, the man currently serving as director of Abruzzo National Park, seemed to offer change to those worried about nefarious influences in the parks. Though he had previously been director at Gran Sasso and Monti della Laga National Park, he had been out of the park rotation for nearly a decade before his name finally made it to the top of the list for Abruzzo. He had several times come close, and each time, his time at Gran Sasso seemed to stand as the primary marker for his qualifications to direct Abruzzo National Park.

Gran Sasso and Monti della Laga National Park is well known not only in Italy but across Europe. Barely fifteen miles north of Abruzzo National Park, Gran Sasso is named after the park's signature mountain. The peak, its name loosely translated as "Great Stone," rises above Abruzzo's wine country and casts a long shadow over the plains that lead down to the sea. A massif with impossible cliffs along its sides, it represents Abruzzo to Italians in the same way that Half Dome represents Yosemite to Americans. Thrust up during what geologists call the Tortonian period ten million years ago, the mountain stands like a great sentinel and is visible from virtually every direction. A sheer slab of limestone along its western face drops thousands of feet down to verdant valleys, where piles of broken rock gird the base of the mountain. Deep gorges and underground tunnels formed by snowmelt crisscross the slopes, carved out of the karst topography that dominates the area. Active fault lines continue to trigger earthquakes throughout the region, including a 2016 rumbler whose epicenter was just a bit farther north in Umbria. The region's most populated city, L'Aquila, just to the west of Gran Sasso, regularly feels tremors, and its 2009 earthquake, which killed more than 300 people, was a catastrophic reminder that the mountains continue to thrust as the tectonic plates shift beneath Italy and reshape the European continent. To this day, construction cranes dominate the skyline of L'Aquila, daily reminders of the 2009 quake's destruction.

Despite the violence of the earthly forces that formed it, the area around Gran Sasso has a reputation as a peaceful and quiet region, known for its slow pace and casual mountain culture. Sometimes called "Little Tibet," Gran Sasso is Himalayan in landscape and attitude. Sheep herding persists, as do the quiet rivalries between ancient hilltop villages. High up in the Gran Sasso in an isolated cauldron, the mountain hides the southernmost glacier in all of Europe, which continues to carve away at the rock. The Calderone glacier, like most glaciers around the world, is melting at an alarming rate, having lost more than 90 percent of its size and volume over the last century. Most scientists believe that it will disappear within the next decade, possibly as early as 2020, taking with it not only an ongoing source of water for the valleys below but an entire ecosystem. The alpine meadows just below the peak rely on the cool air that drops down from the glacier throughout the summer, and many of the streams once fed by the glacier are dry. The crevasses and canyons, which only a decade ago echoed with the rush of glacial water, now sit silent and empty.

The once gradual and now pitched loss of Gran Sasso's alpine ecosystem is part of what led to the creation of the park in 1991, in a flurry of conservation activity in Italy at the close of the twentieth century. Under pressure from the international community and Italian activists like Franco Tassi, and after several studies confirmed the remarkable diversity of life within the unique ecosystem there, the Italian government formed the park. With its creation, the province of Abruzzo became the most protected in Italy, with over one-third of its land area set aside for conservation. By contrast, Tuscany, renowned for its landscape, has barely 400 square miles of national park protection, smaller than just about any county in Texas.

By the time Febbo took over at Gran Sasso in the late 1990s, he had published many articles as both scientist and journalist, including some on the Abruzzo bears in the early part of that decade, and he had become a rather visible advocate for change. He had been involved with Legambiente, one of the largest environmental groups in Italy, and some environmental groups, such as Italy's Green Report, would later praise Febbo's "militancy" while leading Gran Sasso through difficulties with agricultural interests vying for control of the land. By the time he had ascended to lead Gran Sasso and Monti della Laga National Park, his reputation was as a person who demanded closer adherence to park regulations. New development or new incursions by ranchers were stopped, and cattle ranchers in particular had to more closely account for their herds.

In Italy, livestock owners must declare the number of cows they own and ensure that all of their animals are appropriately vaccinated and treated for diseases like tuberculosis. Once a cow has been cleared as healthy and free to graze, it is given an identification tag. The system was, and is, cumbersome and full of bureaucratic pitfalls, but the process aims to ensure safety for both the animals and the consumers of animal goods. It also aims to prevent the spread of disease from domestic to wild animals. Dario Febbo led an attempt to ensure cattle were appropriately declared and registered in Gran Sasso.

Despite all the work Febbo did in Gran Sasso to ensure cattle were registered and had been inspected, his reputation as an enforcer did not carry over when, in 2011, he was finally anointed director of Abruzzo National Park. Problems within Abruzzo National Park suggest that livestock herds in the Abruzzo bears' territory have escaped oversight, with an especially widely covered event in 2014, when a female bear died of tuberculosis. It was the first known case of TB in an Italian bear and, at first, baffled scientists. An autopsy, however, revealed that the TB bacterium that killed the breeding-age female was a bovine strain. The bear had fed on the carcass of a cow and picked up the disease. Researchers were able through DNA testing to pinpoint the precise cow whose infected carrion killed the bear.

At first, park officials strenuously denied any problem with tuberculosis, but as the autopsy results became public, they were forced to acknowledge that the disease likely came from poor oversight of herds in the park. The park resisted suggestions that illegal tagging or failure to have animals inspected or inoculated may have caused the bear's death, but the outcry was strong enough to demand a response from the park. Febbo, as though reliving his days at Gran Sasso, was faced with livestock controversy and the specter of illegal herding.

The park's response was, for most conservationists, too slow and too measured. As more than one researcher pointed out, a TB epidemic would end the bear species, so they wanted swift action. They pressured Febbo and others in the administration, but most ultimately felt that the park lacked the sense of urgency needed to address the problem. Some called for the herds to be removed altogether until a full accounting could be made.

And yet the herds remained. Ranchers continued their operations, and those who would defend the bears found themselves confronting the possibility that forces that influenced the cattle industry in other parts of Italy may have finally found a foothold in the mountains of Abruzzo.

# 24

## The Blue Snow of Abruzzo

In 2013, Bruno D'Amicis pressed deep into the mountains of Abruzzo National Park, seeking out high rocky outcrops from which to observe bears. It was late winter, at a time when the first signs of spring had started to appear, but in the high mountain passes, ice still clung to rocks like lichen. Drifts of snow glittered with crystalline light in shadowed escarpments. D'Amicis had just begun a new ascent after a brief pause in his climb when, head down and focused on the path in front of him, he stumbled onto something bizarre. Along the trail, he noticed that some of the snow was blue.

Not a subtle blue.

Not a blueish shade of white.

Blue. Absolute blue.

He had never seen anything like it. Despite years wandering the hills and valleys of Abruzzo, he had never encountered a blue like this.

He walked the area around the blue snow, tracing its contours and looking for a local cause—an unusual plant or fungus, a water source, an insect. Nothing.

He bent close, thinking the odd snow might have an odor, but he could not discern a smell. He touched it and considered tasting it, but thought better of it. Especially odd was that the blue snow was in a line, in drops, leading up the trail. He could not imagine what it was, but he felt certain it was not natural. He was also certain it was not good.

D'Amicis is more than simply a keen observer of nature. He has significant training in natural history, and he has spent his career advocating for wildlife. While a young man in Rome, he studied biology under Luigi Boitani. D'Amicis, however, is not a scientist. He is an internationally renowned wildlife photographer, and he has forged a reputation for creating wildlife imagery that changes the world.

A native of the Eternal City, D'Amicis moved to the mountains after his studies under Boitani because he witnessed the ongoing degradation of the land and felt he had to act. Science alone, he felt, was not going to address the issues he saw in front of him. He wanted to do something others could relate to, and he wanted to convey to others the beauty he saw in the world around him. Science provided insight into the things he witnessed, but photography provided him with an opportunity to share the natural world's beauty and meaning with broader audiences.

When he stumbled on the blue snow in the heart of Abruzzo, he was not conducting scientific research. He had long since left intensive study under Boitani and others in Rome, and while Boitani's influence on him is clear, it ultimately serves only as a foundation for a different kind of exploration of nature and wildlife. D'Amicis's work now focuses on not simply documenting species around the globe but doing so with the explicit purpose of motivating people to act on behalf of nature.

D'Amicis began taking photographs of rare species almost immediately after leaving university, carving out a name for himself as a photographer with eminent patience and keen timing, a combination that allows him to capture remarkable and fleeting moments and share them with the world. His photography, which has appeared in just about every major wildlife publication in the world, started with images of Abruzzo's native flora and fauna but has since expanded significantly. He has traveled the globe seeking out new vistas and new visions of nature.

D'Amicis's reputation, which had been steadily growing over a decade, was solidified in 2010 when he published a book of photographs of the Tichá Valley in Slovakia. Loosely translated as the "Silent Valley," its pristine wilderness has been largely untouched over the last century, thanks to special protections put in place decades ago. It is home to a variety of large mammals, including wolves and brown bears, yet it is threatened on all sides by clear-cutting and extensive natural resource extraction. D'Amicis's book, *The Last Stronghold*, was a collaboration with Erik Baláž, a Slovak who has a long history of engagement with wilderness issues in the area. The two published the book on their own dime, believing that development around the park warranted immediate action. They apparently hit a nerve.

The large volume sold out within a year, providing a burst of income for the two and leading to a remarkable change in Slovakia. The book was in no small part responsible for a public outcry that led to greater protections of the wilderness area and expanded protections in areas just around the Tichá Valley. Though much of the surrounding land is part of the Tatra National Park, it had been widely exploited, and the book helped stem the tide and secure a safe zone for wildlife. In short, it ensured that the silence that gave the land its name remained.

D'Amicis has pressed forward with similar work in his own country. He has published a book on the chamois, a rare species of European antelope that, until recently, hovered on the brink of extinction. Now recovering and spreading in range, the chamois are an indicator species that speak to the ecological health of a region. They thrive in alpine habitat and are often visible in Abruzzo National Park clinging to mountainsides in the same way that mountain goats cling to cliff faces in the Rocky Mountains. They feed on a variety of plant life, and in turn, they and the local roe deer provide prey for wolves. D'Amicis's book on the chamois documented not just the beauty of the animals and their feats of acrobatics in the high Abruzzi but also the astonishing recovery that is possible when the value of an animal is recognized and forces are marshaled to preserve them.

D'Amicis also turned his attention to the wolves of Abruzzo, publishing a book in 2015 on the unique packs that roam Abruzzo National Park and its environs. As with all of his books, the photographs are accompanied by D'Amicis's observations and assessments of the state of the environment, yet the force of each book is its imagery and photography's ability to transport the viewer into another world. Jim Brandenburg, an Ely, Minnesota-based American photographer of worldwide fame thanks to his photographs of North American wolves, penned a foreword to the book.

By the time he published his wolf book, D'Amicis had realized a certain level of celebrity in the world of nature photography. He was named European Nature Photographer of the Year and then, at a dazzling gala in London, was anointed Wildlife Photographer of the Year. He takes those honors in stride, recognizing them as important to his career but not to his life in the wild. In recent years, he has even found himself facing difficult internal questions about the meaning and significance of his work and whether, as a photographer in the digital age, his work can make a difference. He wonders about photography's capacity to foster change.

What that change looks like in terms of the Abruzzo bear is not entirely clear, and D'Amicis himself struggles with how to approach the dilemma of the most important species in the park. Despite offers and opportunities to produce a book on the bears of Abruzzo, he has not yet done it. He is admittedly conflicted about a project.

On the one hand, he has made thousands of photographs of the bears. He has stalked them with his camera; camped out in rain, ice, and snow with nothing but a parka and his backpack; and effectively lived alongside them on an almost daily basis for more than a decade. If he is not traveling for photo shoots for *National Geographic* or other high-end publishers, he is in Abruzzo, most frequently hoping to catch a glimpse of the bears. On the other hand, D'Amicis realizes that greater awareness of the bears would be a mixed blessing. The bears are in a precarious position, more so than most other animals. Unlike, for instance, awareness about a rare salamander, which is unlikely to result in hordes of tourists seeking it out, greater awareness of the bear promises to bring crowds to the park. While such crowds are not inherently a problem for the bears, the impact of such an influx on local culture could upset a delicate balance that is keeping the bears alive. If, however, more people find the Abruzzi a compelling place to live or stay for longer periods, development in the form of tourist services or housing could undermine any attempts to protect the bears from exploitation.

Perhaps more important, it could also aggravate the already tense relationship among various development factions in Abruzzo. As it is, some of the Abruzzese see the tourists who come as, at best, aggravations and, at worst, interlopers who with their "do good" attitudes threaten to disrupt long-standing traditions. Nature lovers from other parts of Europe may hardly attempt to understand the local culture, let alone respect the ways that the local farmers have sought to live with the wildlife and the land. Bear tourists would, in this worldview, probably be the worst possible type of visitor because they would undermine the relationship the people have formed with the animal that is their pride.

Still, D'Amicis knows that such concerns can no longer be the reason to keep the story of the bears to himself. The blue snow drives that point home.

In all likelihood, the blue snow D'Amicis stumbled on that spring day was laced with poison. D'Amicis discussed the discovery with local naturalists, who noted that carrion is often laced with a poison that dramatically discolors the snow. D'Amicis had likely been near a carcass that would have been used as bait to attract "nuisance" animals like wild dogs, wolves, and bears. The dead animal had probably been dragged a short distance from its original location, and the blue snow was residue of the poison laced into the carrion.

The blue snow means that D'Amicis and others like him can no longer keep quiet and can no longer afford to protect the bears by silence. Their voices must be heard, and in the case of D'Amicis, his lens must now show the world what is at stake.

The poisoning of bears is nothing new in the park. It has been a favorite tactic of ranchers who insist, against all evidence, that the bears attack their cows. No data exists to corroborate such claims of bear attacks on livestock, and indeed, the only bits that exist actually demonstrate the opposite. Paolo Ciucci and his researchers have shown time and again that Apennine bears do not each much meat. Their feces, which researchers collect and analyze, has virtually no meat in it, and autopsies of killed bears have even less evidence that they are meat eaters. Further, the meat that researchers actually do find tends to be that of small animals such as mice or foxes, and the remains of any cow or sheep are invariably from carrion that the bears scavenged.

The Abruzzo bears, in other words, do not stalk and eat cows. They never have. They never will. They are simply not adapted to do so.

Cattle herds are a new phenomenon in the area, and the bears of Abruzzo, evolved over thousands of years in an area largely devoid of livestock, simply do not have the bone structure to suggest that they are beef predators. While it is certainly not beyond the realm of possibility that the bears might attack an already injured animal or even a small calf, stories of such attacks are not only rare but largely unsubstantiated. The bears are not a threat to cattle.

Yet the bears continue to be poisoned. According to Federica di Leonardo, a journalist who has covered the plight of the bears, poisonings have been the top cause of bear mortality since 2000, outstripping natural death, vehicle collisions, and shootings. In 2013, more than thirty poisoned baits were found within the park, resulting in the death of wolves, foxes, and, park officials suspect, an eagle. On one occasion, a hiker discovered a bait trap, and a special team of forest service rangers canvassed the area, removing the baits before a bear could be killed. The rangers failed, however, to uncover the culprits.

The poisoning of Abruzzo's bears made international headlines for a brief period in 2007, when an especially well-known and beloved bear was killed. Bernardo the bear was known for his antics in the valley just outside of Pescasseroli. He often posed for pictures, seemingly enamored of tourist attention and savoring his status as park celebrity. He was so well known among locals and tourists alike that Abruzzo National Park started to use him as a centerpiece of their campaign, to increase not only environmental tourism but wildlife awareness as well. Bernardo's kind demeanor and somewhat mischievous nature—he had a habit of scavenging local trash cans and gardens for quick snacks—brought widespread attention to the bears. Bernardo also provided an opportunity for education. Some thought Bernardo too habituated to human activity, and though no one ever reported a threatening encounter with him, park officials believed he represented an animal that could both embody the ideals of the park and educate the public about the need for the animals to have more space, more room to roam, and more wilderness in which to live. Bernardo was photogenic, but he was also the embodiment of genuine need for change.

When the body of Bernardo was found in 2007, he was not alone. The poison trap also killed two other bears. Bernardo's mate was found alongside him, and a short distance away, a male cub was also found dead. Images of the killings, almost immediately made public, showed a grotesque scene. Vacant-eyed Bernardo lay stretched out in the weeds, as though pulling himself away. Flies, congregating on the corpse, are visible on his snout.

If Ciucci's estimates that forty to fifty total bears remain is even close to accurate (and it is), one poison trap had killed nearly 10 percent of the population. It was, as one official noted, a massacre, and the images of Bernardo's body drove home the point. Bernardo, whose lively existence had been documented in innumerable tourist photographs, now appeared in papers and magazines and on the Internet as a desiccated, lifeless heap. Later, it would be revealed that the poisoned bait had even greater impact than had first been suspected: Besides the three bears, it had also killed five wolves, eighteen boars, and ten vultures. It was, indeed, a massacre.

Park leadership was devastated by Bernardo's death, and outrage spread across the region. Environmental groups called for action, with the World Wildlife Fund issuing a €10,000 bounty on the killer. The Italian Green party, an active part of the Italian political system, matched it. Italy's top environment minister labeled the killings an assault not just on the rare bears but on the park system itself, and he called for an immediate crackdown on poaching and all illegal activity in any of Abruzzo's parks, from Abruzzo to Gran Sasso to Majella. News media swarmed, with features about the incident running even in major US newspapers such as *USA Today*, whose headline read, "Italian Officials Hunt for Killers of 3 Endangered Bears."

Despite the international attention, the government's declarations, and the bounty, no one was ever arrested for killing Bernardo and the others. Rumors persist to this day as to the culprit, and many inside the park readily share the name of the person they suspect. Yet no one was indicted or prosecuted, and within a couple of years, the poisonings began again. Usually taking the lives of domestic animals and wild dogs, they hit wolves, boars, and foxes especially hard. One study indicates that between 2005 and 2009, more than 4,500 cases of poisoned animals resulting in death occurred in Italy, yet that number does not include reports from Abruzzo, where such records were unobtainable due to both lack of funding and lack of will to report the deaths. Abruzzo, Sicily, and Sardinia remain the areas with the greatest number of poisonings, and yet none track their numbers in any reliable or consistent way.

Since Bernardo's death, the government and not-for-profits have adopted new measures to try to prevent more bear poisonings. One project, called Life Pluto, aims to teach the public to identify potentially poisonous baits and report them. It provides a nationwide number to call in the event that someone sees suspicious carcasses or witnesses unusual activity that might indicate a poison trap. Another project, Antidoto, uses specially trained dogs to sniff out and retrieve poison traps before they kill wild animals. Two units of these dogs have been trained and deployed to try to track down suspicious material, and the Antidoto team has evolved to be a core element of Life Pluto.

The retrieval of thirty poison traps inside Abruzzo National Park in 2013 suggests that the results of such programs have been modest. On the one hand, park officials were able to locate the traps. On the other hand, the audacity of setting such large numbers of poison traps *inside* a national park suggests that someone, or some group, has little respect for the officials trying to stop the activity. And of course, more than one official has expressed concern that those thirty traps could simply be the tip of the proverbial iceberg. The only way to stop the poisonings will be to arrest and prosecute those who set them.

In small, tight-knit communities like those in and around Abruzzo, identifying culprits can be difficult. No one wants to be a rat, even if they do not approve of the activity. Further, the traps may not be the work of the local population. While poisoning was legal in Italy until the mid-1970s and had become a habit among the farmers and landowners throughout the country, most have long since adapted to the laws and changed their ways of doing things. If they have a nuisance animal, they find other ways than poison to deal with it. But individuals who are already more likely to be engaged in illegal activity find little reason to follow that particular law. They solve their problems the way they want to, regardless of law, edict, or code.

No one will go on record to say that livestock herdsmen are responsible for the poisonings. While many murmur to that effect and some insist that the ranchers, connected to the mob, have access to poisons in ways that locals do not, no one has been able to demonstrate any definitive link. There may not be. It could be that local farmers, annoyed with the government, the park, or simply their neighbors, continue to use poison to lure and kill animals they do not want around. If so, local solutions, such as providing financial compensation for any losses from wildlife incursions, should be sufficient to curb the illegal activity. Such measures have proven effective in places around the world, but in Abruzzo, they are not. The standard methods of dealing with wildlife killings do not seem to work, and one reasonable conclusion would be that those methods do not address the underlying cause of the problems. Few dare say it out loud, but those problems are potentially the same that Antoci faces in Sicily, and the only solution is aggressive legal action. Educational campaigns and poison-sniffing dogs simply will not be sufficient. The entire industry that makes poisoning profitable will have to be taken down.

# 25

~~~~~~

# Rewilding the Mob

For nearly four years, Bruno D'Amicis worked for an organization called Rewilding Europe. He was part of an ambitious hiring campaign by the Italian branch of the organization, and he was part of a plan to broker a deal with the cattlemen to try to change the fate of the bears.

D'Amicis is keenly aware of the forces conspiring to undermine bear conservation in Abruzzo National Park. While he maintains a healthy skepticism toward both rumors of malfeasance and the inefficiencies of Italian park governance, he also knows that local protocols are effectively useless when the entire park system has been undermined. Whether it be through the politicization of park appointments or the dark influence of renegades, change for the park, he knows, will meet tremendous resistance. His hope while working for Rewilding was that extending the proverbial olive branch, attempting to work with instead of against the system, would facilitate enduring change. And his hope for change nearly came to be.

As part of the Rewilding program, D'Amicis and other important members of the organization helped develop a plan that would address both the needs of the cattle industry and the needs of the park. They arranged an effective ceasefire between the local ranching interests and local wildlife while they developed an innovative—indeed entrepreneurial—plan. The Rewilding team decided that speaking the language of money would bring change, so they imagined what financial obstacles might prevent the ranchers from changing the way they grazed their cattle. By eliminating those obstacles, they would pave the way for a new peace in the region. Rewilding would be able to claim another conservation win, and the cattle grazers would be able to claim that they had helped with park conservation while still profiting handsomely from their work.

The park was eager to see the deal done.

Local politicians were as well.

The Rewilding team and the ranchers seemed united in their desire to make a deal.

Everything seemed to be falling into place. Until it didn't.

Rewilding prides itself on innovative deal making and a willingness to think outside the box in order to accomplish its goals. Officially launched in 2011, the organization's primary goal is to make Europe more wild. The group is, however, careful in delineating precisely what that means. While group members certainly hope to return some parts of Europe to more pristine wilderness, they recognize that such a goal is not only unrealistic in some areas, but also too limiting for the organization itself. So they think of *rewilding* as a process by which local stakeholders can make natural processes the center of decision-making. In areas close to or within cities, returning a landscape to wilderness is a pipe dream, but encouraging city development to consider how it might work with nature and the natural processes in that area to integrate wilderness as part of everyday life is not. If development recognizes the value of "the wild," whatever that may look like in a given place, it can reconceive of itself as part of natural processes, not simply oppositional to them.

The approach has led to notable successes with urban and suburban residents, but in rural areas, the group has had the largest impact. Rewilding Europe remains primarily focused on locating and securing wild areas that might be preserved or returned to a more purely wild state in order to preserve native species that rely on wilderness. Their approach is decidedly entrepreneurial and capitalistic: Instead of waiting for governments to create nature preserves or parks, they kick-start green initiatives and economies as a way to expand a conservation ethic and incentivize local participation in rewilding efforts. By directing resources not only to preservation but also to new entrepreneurial activity that might create durable changes to local economies, they hope not only to create more wilderness but also to put in place support systems that are inextricably tied to rewilded land.

The approach is savvy but not without controversy. The program is underwritten to various degrees by state agencies like the European Commission, Dutch and Swedish lottery foundations, and not-for-profits like the European Nature Trust and the World Wildlife Fund. Bringing together such diverse constituents, many of whom may be vested in funding projects in specific localities, creates negotiation challenges. Complex relationships must be honored, of course, as do obligations to follow initiatives sponsored by funding organizations.

Nonetheless, Rewilding has brought together a wide range of conservationists and environmental activists to advance an agenda across much of Europe. The group helped preserve a remarkably untouched wetland where the Danube flows into the Black Sea, furthered and supported initiatives to preserve vast regions in Lapland in the far north of Europe, and moved to preserve enormous stretches of land in Romania and Bulgaria. Their work in the latter two illustrates a particularly important vision of the organization, which is to identify and protect areas—especially those in former Soviet Eastern Bloc nations—that have been abandoned due to collapse of nation-states or lack of economic opportunity. Areas that development has left behind can be more easily recovered, preserved, and rewilded on a far larger scale than in more economically advantaged areas.

Still, the organization recognizes that to maintain the rewilding project in those areas, it needs to boost economic activity. It has, accordingly, invested in green economies. Through a program called Rewilding Europe Capital, it funds initiatives like "European safari" outfits that provide tours of rewilded areas, the training and employment of nature guides, and providing capital for innovative business that might thrive in a project area. It offers highly competitive, low-interest loans to new businesses whose economic development in rewilded areas is built on a conservation ethic. In short, it funds companies that rely on wilderness so that they, in turn, will work to maintain the wild themselves.

It is this aspect of Rewilding that Bruno D'Amicis thought might finally bring hope to the bears of Abruzzo. The organization identified the central Apennines as ideal for pursuing rewilding work, and D'Amicis saw opportunity for change. With national parks already established in the central range of the mountains, a long-standing respect of nature by locals, and the slow but sure flight of most young people out of the region, the area around Abruzzo National Park seemed ideal. It had a degree of wilderness already, but with a thinning population, it provided opportunity to rewild areas that had as yet not been claimed for conservation. D'Amicis, already known for his work in Slovakia, was a natural choice to join the organization.

D'Amicis, whose photography career was thriving when he first considered working for Rewilding, thought twice about joining. It would require him to cut back on some of his more exotic on-site photo shoots, and it would tighten demand on his time. He would continue his photography with the organization to provide them with compelling imagery, but he would now be saddled with certain administrative duties. It would require him as well to work within an organizational system that would be quite different from the freelance career he had carved out for himself. The potential to help his home country, however, overcame his doubts.

Rewilding launched its foray into Italy by focusing on the plight of the parks in Abruzzo and the animals that roam there. D'Amicis used his talents to make incredible photographs that told the story of the region. The images for the organization began to appear in all sorts of media outlets, and D'Amicis turned his attention to making the Abruzzi familiar to all Italians. High mountain valleys, stoic chamois sitting atop outcroppings, wolves and bears wandering forest and glen, and sunrises across crags white with late-spring snow provided a vision of possibility for the region. It may be only a short drive from Rome, the images seemed to say, but it is a wilderness worth exploring.

D'Amicis was also working in other ways to reverse the collapse of the Abruzzo bear population. The Italian branch of Rewilding Europe met time and again to strategize and to develop practical plans that might address the primary obstacles to bear repopulation. They discussed limiting road development, helping local businesses rethink their relationship with the national parks and the as-yet-undeveloped lands surrounding them, and fostering green tourism as a long-term employment opportunity for locals. All this would be helpful in rewilding the area, but one major issue would need to be addressed first: cattle grazing.

So they developed a plan. Their approach was pragmatic: Meet with the cattlemen and broker a deal. While everyone recognized that other forces behind the scenes would not directly deal with an organization like Rewilding, D'Amicis hoped that negotiating with ranchers and providing them with options would lead the underwriters of the operations to follow the lead of men working the land. And, to add incentive, Rewilding made a deal that they believed even a group like, say, the Mafia could not resist. They would reimburse the ranchers for any cost they incurred to change their operations. Indeed, they would pay the herd owners to move their livestock.

In recent years, a similar but less expensive program launched in Gran Sasso and Monti della Laga National Park. Working under a project called Life Praterie, a group of Gran Sasso park officials initiated a series of town hall gatherings and individual meetings with livestock owners and residents. The Life Praterie program aims to preserve the distinctive grasslands of portions of Gran Sasso, which are man-made, cleared by humans several generations ago for grazing primarily sheep. Over time, the grasslands developed a special ecology that now houses unique species of plants and small animals. The grasslands require grazing to maintain their distinctive ecosystem, but with thousands of head of cattle replacing sheep, they also require management. The Gran Sasso team decided that instead of prohibiting, they would simply guide cattle in order to bring greater adherence to park policy. There, it seems to be working, but in Abruzzo National Park, the stakes are higher because more species are under direct threat from cattle ranching. Rewilding's plan, entrepreneurial and innovative, appeared to be the perfect fit for Abruzzo National Park and its cattle problems.

The offer was attractive, if not outright audacious. Rewilding had already identified an area to relocate the cattle herds, one far from prime bear habitat. They would enclose the new area with high-quality fencing, build new barns for the livestock with the latest technology for animal maintenance, help corral the herds and transport them, and cover any losses during transport. And, of course, the new land would still be, at least in part, on park land, so the ranchers (and their investors) would not have to worry about new expenses associated with land leases. In return, the ranchers would simply agree to keep their operations at the new location and allow the bear habitat to rewild.

It was a sweetheart deal. Rewilding would pay for almost everything. The livestock owners faced no out-of-pocket expenses yet received significant upgrades to part of their business. In return, all they had to do was keep the cattle away from the central valley of the park.

After soft-touch negotiating and, apparently, approval from their underwriters, the ranchers agreed to the deal. Rewilding accomplished what others had been unable to do simply by appealing to what mattered most: the bottom line. No one believed a deal was possible, but all it required was capital from an environmental organization willing to focus on the big picture of conservation and set aside more rigid solutions based on impossible ideals. Real-world negotiating backed by entrepreneurial minds and dedicated activists led to a plan that would finally secure some measure of safety for the bears from their greatest threat.

D'Amicis was ecstatic. "It was too good to pass up. No one could refuse that offer. We were covering everything. All they had to do was say okay, and they would have brand-new farms and fresh new fields for grazing. It was perfect."

The deal was so exciting that the mayor of Gioia dei Marsi arranged for a ceremonial signing of it. The mayor, representatives from Rewilding, and members of the cattle industry were slated to gather to finalize the deal. The paperwork was completed and had been reviewed by attorneys. It had the feel of a peace deal, where long-warring parties were finally coming together to break the stalemate. Joy—genuine joy—spread among the members of the Rewilding team.

It would not last. Just as the deal was to be signed, the ranchers brought the process to a screeching halt. They did not show up. They apparently decided that one particular part of the agreement—the part that indicated that they were responsible for keeping the cows in the new location once they had been relocated there—was too burdensome.

At first, it seemed like a joke. Then, a minor road bump. But then it became clear among members of the Rewilding group that a wall was being erected. The cows, the herdsmen said, get out of their fences all the time. They would probably remember the old grazing grounds and return.

The ranchers never signed the deal and never bothered to show up to discuss the matter. The Rewilding contingent could barely contain their shock and frustration. They had done everything possible not only to make it attractive but also to make it profitable. And the bears—the bears would have peace.

But it was not enough. The forces that drive the cattle industry saw something they did not like. The proclaimed reason was that pesky cows are hard to track down and control, but that is not only fundamentally untrue, it is absurd. A cattle rancher's job is to control herds, mend fences, and pasture in ideal locations. So the real reason, lingering somewhere in the back rooms of people whom no one really knows but everyone fears, is likely linked to something else. Money. Influence. Control. Power. It could even just be pettiness. It will never be known.

But what is clear is that the deal's collapse marked the beginning of the end of Rewilding's influence in the area. What was going to be a major success was turned immediately into a crippling failure, and within only a couple of years, core members of the Rewilding team, including D'Amicis, would leave the organization disappointed, disaffected, and despondent.

# PART V: RESURRECTING THE WILD

# 26

Save the Bears

For many people heartbroken by the lost opportunity for change, something new seemed not only necessary but also urgent. The bears must be defended. If their land could not be reclaimed, and if their habitat could not be fully protected by a large international organization, then someone had to step in and police the situation. In 2013, during a particularly trying time when people like D'Amicis and Ciucci began to deeply question their ability to facilitate change and make a difference, new defenders came. The group, Salviamo l'Orso, was the creation of Italian nature lovers and activists, and its goal is to act as a stop-gap measure to protect the bears until greater cultural change occurs.

The principal of Salviamo is Stefano Orlandini. Orlandini, a native of Naples who spends much of each year in Kazakhstan, convened a small group of volunteers to launch an aggressive campaign to save the Abruzzo bears. His organization, run largely through the goodwill of volunteers and ad hoc employees like one especially active advocate, Mario Cipollone, would be the first activist group whose sole purpose was to establish and implement a plan to protect and save the bears.

Salviamo functions as one part educator, one part watchdog, and one part partner with the park. The organization tries to be visible and pragmatic with its projects, and people like Cipollone work on various initiatives within and around the borders of the park to maintain a clear presence. For example, they created road signs for high-risk bear crossing areas. RALLENTARE! the signs read: WARNING! Orange and a bit larger than the size of a speed limit sign, the signage required multiple levels of vetting despite its simplicity and obvious benefit. As Cipollone explains, even though the signs would cost nothing for the park—Salviamo l'Orso was footing the entire bill—archaic rules initially prohibited their being erected. For instance, they could not be placed as close to the road as an official roadway sign because statutes protected road right-of-ways for only official signage. Even though the warning signs were a collaboration with park officials, and even though they received the blessing of more than one governmental body, they had to be placed a couple of feet farther away from the road than state road signs.

Salviamo l'Orso began an education campaign for landowners just outside the park boundaries. Salviamo personnel teach residents how best to dispose of trash, where best to place livestock, and how best to fence land to protect small hobby-farm animals. They even provide electrical fencing and conduct yearly maintenance tests to ensure fences remain fully functional. The goal is to provide locals with both resources and knowledge to prevent destructive bear-human interactions. The park has even joined in this effort, launching its own electrical fencing initiative, and despite many of the landowners preferring the materials provided by Salviamo, the park's actions suggest that when officials sense positive developments, they can still be persuaded to act.

The relationship between Salviamo l'Orso and the park, however, is complicated. Salviamo recently signed an agreement of cooperation with the park, but even after the signing, Salviamo has demonstrated that it is prepared to blow the whistle on any lapses in park oversight and that it is swift to act on behalf of the bears.

Salviamo l'Orso has assumed, then, the role of protector. While Rewilding Europe aimed to fundamentally change a system by working within that system's constraints, Salviamo is taking a zero-tolerance stance on issues that directly impact the bears. A tiny not-for-profit, its ability to act is limited, but its laser focus on the bears has ensured its effectiveness. It has quickly gained a reputation for risking direct intervention through legal processes if necessary, and the organization insists that it will work to preserve the bears while other larger organizations come and go. The World Wildlife Fund, which at opportune moments appears on the scene to proffer opinions or protest activities, has, like Rewilding Europe, had too many other projects to focus on, so it is only small organizations like Salviamo that stand in the way of the ultimate destruction of the bears. Salviamo is the last line of defense, the last real hope for preservation, until a confederation of groups both within and outside of Italy can coalesce into a viable movement to effect long-term change. Until then, preservation of the remnant bear population within the boundaries of the park requires officials to resist incursions by criminals, and it requires watchdog groups like Salviamo to sniff out and raise the alarm about any intruders. It is a waiting game, a hope for preservation against all reasonable signs that preservation is even possible.

Preservation, however, may not be the only path. Another avenue to the Abruzzo bears' survival may have recently presented itself, one that suggests that even if tragedy occurs and the bears pass away, resurrection may be possible. If the bears, like so many wild animals over the last century, succumb to the overwhelming forces that seem bent on their extermination, there may yet be a way to bring them back from the abyss.

It seems like science fiction, but in fact, biologists are on the cusp of a discovery that promises to change the future of conservation. It is a discovery whose center of gravity is central Europe, not far from Abruzzo National Park, and by a strange twist of fate, one of the central figures in it is deeply invested in the survival of the Abruzzo bears.

His name is Pasqualino Loi, and he has an audacious, if not entirely mad, plan to save the Abruzzo bears.

He wants to clone them.

And it appears he may be able to do it.

# 27

~~~~~

# Loi and Loss

In the village of Nepezzano, on the outskirts of Teramo, Italy, Lino Loi prepares for a feast. He is hosting a farewell dinner for a group of graduate students who have come from Poland to study with him during a summer short course. The town is wedged between Gran Sasso and the Adriatic Sea in Abruzzo, and from Loi's home, both sea and mountain are visible on a clear day. It is, as the crow flies, only thirty-five miles from Abruzzo National Park.

Loi grills ribs and prepares eggplant in a rich red sauce. Beer sits alongside, of all things, boxed wine, and *pane carasau*, a thin, crispy flatbread, occupies sections of a long wooden table that stretches across a single-room barn Loi renovated to accommodate gatherings of friends and family. The table seats at least twenty people, and as Loi surveys the preparations, he says, "With bread, you will never die."

Sardinian, Loi is full of colloquial wisdom. He prefers simple meals, and he is quick to laugh. He is even more quick to fill an empty plate or glass. His graduate students arrive essentially en masse, and above the din of wine-induced relaxation, Loi laughs, applauds, and praises each person who has come. He is in his element.

Affable and gracious, he prides himself on his hospitality. He attributes his warmth to his Sardinian heritage as surely as he attributes his love of the land to his family and the island life of his youth. He lives in a home adjacent to a historic fountain, and when he renovated the house and its accompanying small barn, construction crews uncovered Roman artifacts alongside Nazi tools. The fountain supplied the area with its drinking water since before recorded history, and the homestead, built much later, was occupied by the Germans during World War II. Loi, when prompted, produces pieces of Roman glass and a scythe with a swastika emblazoned on its blade. He clearly adores the historical importance of his property, and he declares that when he retires, he will begin a new life as an archaeologist and travel the world to dig through ruins and resurrect their stories.

That instinct to breathe new life into old stories is, in some ways, at the heart of his career now, and if he senses possibilities in archaeology to make things new again, his work in animal science probes the frontiers of knowledge to resurrect the past. In doing so, he hopes to ensure a more vibrant future.

Loi is a pioneer in the field of genetic conservation. Working with state-of-the-art cloning technology, he aims to save species, and when the technology to reach his goal does not exist, he invents it. In the case of animal cloning, he has created a revolutionary new process to preserve and, most remarkably, transfer DNA from one animal to another.

Loi's interest in science and animal life began when he was a young boy. He remembers childhood in Sardinia as a daily adventure. He roamed the land around the family home, he helped his father split wood and tend to the land, and he explored the outdoors virtually every day. Animals were everywhere: rabbits, field mice, birds. He loved it.

Thinking back on that time, he grows nostalgic. "It's not like it was," he says. "That life is disappearing." While he means the agrarian life of rural Sardinia, the statement weighs more heavily. He sees the entire world around him changing, from the slow degradation of wildlife habitat to the loss of species, from the erosion of a special kind of Sardinian pride in kindness to even the loss of his own connection to the land and his Sardinian heritage.

Loi was one of the first scientists to work on a technique called *nuclear transfer*, which is essentially the process of transplanting a cell from one embryo or individual into an enucleated egg, previously deprived of its own chromosomes. The process is a method of asexual reproduction commonly called *cloning*. Loi had been among the team of scientists who worked with Dolly the sheep on the groundbreaking, headline-making cloning project in Scotland. Dolly was the first mammal ever to be cloned, and from 1996 to 2003, she lived the life of a scientific celebrity. She was on the cover of major magazines, and her birth launched a broad discussion about the ethics of cloning. What were its limits? What should governments allow scientists to do? How far should the technology be allowed to advance? Can we, or should we, clone humans?

Dolly renewed popular interest in science, and during the late 1990s she became synonymous with both scientific progress and, for some, the hubris of the human mind. On the one hand, she represented the capacity for science to change the world; on the other hand, she embodied humanity's attempt to trump nature or God and to become a creator. Dolly herself would later become a mother many times over, breeding successfully and producing not just single offspring but twins and triplets. By just about any measure, she was an astounding success, even if she animated discussion of complex ethical questions about humans' ability to alter life on Earth.

Loi worked in the background of the Dolly project, but his role was not insignificant. The lead scientists eventually won the Nobel Prize for their work, but Loi and a couple of other scientists like him were passed over in the formal proclamation. Later, he would receive a letter acknowledging the oversight and officially recognizing his role. It was a polite letter but hardly full acknowledgment of his, or others', contributions.

That acknowledgment, however, was then and remains today secondary to Loi's career. He never sought praise, and, without prying, no one would even know he had been so deeply involved in the project. He has pressed forward with his work and left the politics of science behind. The truth for Loi is that Dolly lit a fire in him, and since that project, he has continued to press the boundaries of cloning technology to try to entirely reshape the direction of science.

Shortly after Dolly was cloned, Loi began to see the entire project as too limited in its scope. While a necessary first step in changing science's relationship to the creation of life, it nonetheless stopped short of revolutionizing how science might use cloning to change the world. Dolly was a species of sheep of no particular import, a common breed whose value lay in its capacity to be commodified. The Dolly experiment essentially demonstrated how currently thriving animals might be replicated to expand human industry. Such was not Loi's interest. He saw in cloning the opportunity to preserve animals on the verge of annihilation.

What if, Loi thought, rare animals could be cloned? What if creatures that were near extinction could be saved by a technology like cloning? The prospects enthralled him, and he set about to make it a reality.

To any person with such an agenda, several significant obstacles immediately present themselves. First, and perhaps most obviously, access to endangered species is itself often a problem. Unlike with a sheep, one does not just head down to the local breeder to acquire animals like a lemur, a Florida panther, a Tasmanian devil, or a Marsican bear. So the first step is to ask permission even to look for it. Many of these animals are in protected areas, so the search for the animal itself must be approved by the appropriate authorities. Once that permission is secured, one must ask permission to get close to the animal. Scientists are not asking to simply observe an animal if they intend to clone it: They must touch it, if not tranquilize and capture it. Doing so sometimes requires disturbing pristine natural habitat or making incursions deep into protected areas. Even if they secure permission to venture into preserves to seek out the animal—which is far from guaranteed—they must then ask permission to take a few cells from the animal. That permission in particular is long and complicated, requiring approval from so many state and international bodies that seeking it is full-time work in itself. Not everyone is keen on the idea that a scientist might come to their reserves and sedate an animal in order to poke a needle into it or excise a slice of organ. A country protecting, say, the final fifty survivors of a rare turtle species is not typically eager to offer one of them up for any sort of experimentation, let alone something as untested as cloning. Trying to persuade local and international authorities to take that risk requires persistent engagement and not a small amount of politicking. And, even if one secures such approvals, one still needs funding to travel to and work in the region. Because these are rare animals, simply traveling to and encamping in the animal's habitat does not ensure a chance to collect samples. A scientist on the trail of only fifty known survivors of a given species could spend a lifetime trying to catch a brief glimpse of just one of these animals. And just because a scientist is fortunate enough to see one does not mean he or she will be able to collect cells from it.

Even if a scientist is able to accomplish all of the above, a major obstacle still stands in the way, one that has prevented much of this research from going forward because if it cannot be overcome, all the other issues are simply academic. The issue is simple to understand but until recently virtually impossible to circumvent. Lino Loi appears to have figured it out.

Who will be the mother to the cloned animal? That is the major scientific obstacle. In the case of Dolly, the question seems patently obvious: Another sheep will carry the cloned fetus to term and give birth to it. But what about rare or even extinct animals? How does a scientist secure a female of the species to impregnate, monitor, and help give birth to the cloned offspring? Some endangered animals have a large enough population to allow for science to attempt to implant a fertilized egg into a female. Other species—many other species—do not. In that case, a mother of the same species is just not possible. Either there are not enough, or, in many cases, there may not even be a female left at all. Yet the scientists have the DNA, and they can fertilize an egg. They simply need a host to bring the cloned animal to term.

Loi and his colleagues have developed a system to do that, and it promises to usher in a new scientific era if it is successful. Basically, Loi has figured out how to have one species of animal give birth to an entirely different species.

A goat might give birth to a sheep.

A sheep might give birth to a dog.

A horse might give birth to a rhino.

If Loi's process works, the permutations will be limited only by the imagination. And, of course, the bodies of the mothers.

The frontiers of science have never seemed so bizarre, so challenging, and so full of possibility, both bright and dark.

# 28

Beautiful Minds

Lino Loi steps into his lab. For being home to such startling science, it is remarkably nondescript. About the size of a modest bedroom, its walls are lined with steel and plastic cabinets and built-in desks. Neutral tones and the glimmer of stainless steel instruments give the room the requisite impression of sterility. On one desk is a microscope, something that you would find in any decent lab, and yet it is on this microscope that landmark science is taking place. There, Loi, or sometimes his graduate students, fool animal ova into accepting the DNA of foreign species.

Normally, species keep their genetic identity by breeding within the species, and nature has developed many barriers to protect a species from breeding with others. Typically, when an embryo from a different species is inserted into a host animal, the host body rejects the embryo. In fact, it attacks it, recognizing the foreign DNA within its body and sending cells to destroy the intruder. The egg is effectively sterilized, and the chance at new life ends abruptly.

Early in the development of new life, during what is called the blastocyst stage, embryos grow into a hollow ball of cells in which two different cell types are clearly evident: an inner cell mass (ICM) that generates the fetus proper, and the cells making the trophoblast, a cell mass that generates the placenta. Trophoblast cells establish the contact with the uterine lining and provide stability for the development of life.

Loi's procedure has demonstrated that it is possible to exchange the ICM between sheep embryos and reconstructed embryos that develop into lambs, so he is extending that idea to create a method for fostering life of endangered species. The idea is to isolate by microsurgical procedures the ICM from an embryo of an endangered species, like the white rhino, and to insert it into the trophoblast of a domestic species, like a horse, whose ICM has been removed by microsurgery. The hybrid embryos could then be transferred into the uterus of a mare. The mare's trophoblast would shield the ICM of the wild embryo, thus allowing the mare to, miraculously, deliver a baby rhino. Loi plans to master the technology using different, less high-risk species. In particular, he is piloting the technology by using sheep as foster mothers for roe deer.

The creation of life relies on a set of core processes that results in DNA from two animals fusing together. Sperm and egg, called gametes, bond through a complex set of reactions that allow the DNA within the sperm to join with the DNA in the egg. Both sperm and egg have half the normal number of chromosomes necessary to create life, so when they join, they essentially morph from a half to a whole sequence of DNA. A new genome is created, formed by two interlocking strands of genes. When the sperm penetrates the outer membrane of an egg, the egg spontaneously initiates a series of chemical reactions that, on the one hand, creates a barrier to prevent other sperm from entering, and on the other hand, dissolves the protective layer surrounding the DNA in the head of the sperm. At the same time, the sperm excretes an enzyme that dissolves the outer protection of the gametes to allow access to the female chromosomes. When the chromosomes meet, they fuse and form a zygote. The zygote then begins to replicate, forming a blastocyst. The blastocyst travels to the uterus, where it continues to grow into an embryo and eventually a fetus.

The chemical processes that allow the gametes to join also function to prevent fertilization when unviable DNA mixes occur. The female body has extensive systems of defenses that ensure only "good matches" occur. The host body of the potential embryo intends to protect itself from bad matches not only to ensure possible new life but also to ensure that the host itself is not put at risk.

Loi's system uses those defense systems to his advantage. After an egg is fertilized and morphs into a zygote and then into a blastocyst, the mother's body believes that the developing embryo is already a good match. The outer layers of the blastocyst, the trophoblast, are incredibly resilient and fortified to protect new life, formed for the single purpose of defending the developing life inside it. While it eventually transforms into important parts of the placenta, the trophoblast is essentially the guardian of DNA, and, as far as the mother's body is concerned, important and trustworthy. It is new life coming into existence, so the mother's body creates a strong trophoblast to protect and then later nourish the developing embryo.

Loi realized that attempting to trick a mother's body into believing it could have a "good match" of DNA when it was clearly a bad match was fruitless. He saw, however, that the resilience and formidable cellular structure of the trophoblast provided an exceptional opportunity to help nurture new life. So instead of trying to fertilize across species or introduce new DNA early in the processes of fertilization, he would wait until the blastocyst and the trophoblast were already developed. For the animals he is working with, that is about two days after fertilization. At that point, Loi dissects by microsurgery the ICM from the blastocyst and discards the trophoblast of the roe deer embryo. Next, he dissects the ICM from sheep blastocyst and discards it. He finally injects the roe deer ICM into the sheep trophoblast, completing the procedure.

Much of this process was pioneered by Cesare Galli, an award-winning scientist in veterinary medicine. Galli applied it to artificial reproduction of farm animals, and he has been widely celebrated for his innovations. Loi saw in that work the potential of cross-species birth, and he has been working to demonstrate that it is not only possible but also promising as a way to address the issue of endangered species.

In 2015, Loi was part of a group of scientists who met in Vienna to craft a plan to attempt to clone across species. The members of the group came from universities across Europe, and they developed a protocol and established priorities for the experiment. Loi and his lab were chosen to host the first attempt.

The plan calls for a sheep to give birth to a deer. Loi's graduate students were tapped to assist in the experiment, but Loi himself is the pioneer. "I've waited my whole life for this," he says. Speaking of his graduate students, he says, "They are excellent at the procedure, and I trust them. Really, they are excellent, but I must do this myself."

Similarities between sheep and roe deer make the two species ideal for the experiment. Deer bodies carry a fawn to term after five months, but for four months prior, the embryo essentially sits in the mother's body, turned off or inactive. The mating season for roe deer is late summer and early fall, yet even after the deer has successfully mated, the fertilized egg essentially goes into hibernation, waiting until December or January to begin development. The reason is adaptation. If the embryo began development at the moment of fertilization, the mother would give birth to the fawn in the middle of winter, with very little to eat and with heightened risk of predation (predators are similarly stressed for food during winter months). Somewhere in the deer's genetic history is a program to keep the fertilized egg protected until the mother can give birth at a time of verdant fields and lush vegetation. After four months of quiet non-development, the eggs spark to life and develop into zygotes, then blastocysts, then embryos, until finally, in the bounty of May, the fawns are born.

Loi's experiment will be the first of its kind, but it is not without analogous work or precedent. British researchers discovered this possibility when a sheep delivered a goat. In truth, the animal was a hybrid of the two species, an extraordinarily rare event. Sometimes called a "geep" or a "shoat," the hybrid goat-sheep mix usually dies as an embryo. When one is carried to term, however, it typically surprises the sheep's owner, who is greeted with an unusual critter with a face only a mother could love. Still, the fact that a mother sheep could bring to term an animal that is not a sheep provided researchers with hope—perhaps even evidence—that cross-species delivery of an animal would be possible.

Loi sees in the Vienna project new opportunities to preserve species, and he has surrounded himself with graduate students who share his passion for the impossible and the miraculous. Loi's lab is a melting pot of students from throughout Italy and Europe, full of energy and enthusiasm, if also intensity and focus. English, as a scientific lingua franca, is used to overcome any communication difficulties. Some of the graduate students are already moving into promising careers as researchers who will challenge the boundaries of science. Domenico Iuso has a special passion for the bears of Abruzzo, though he is currently pursuing advanced research in Japan. Luca Palazzese has mastered Loi's processes and has, according to Loi, perhaps the steadiest hand and most delicate touch of his students; he is quiet and intent, and he harbors tremendous love of the outdoors and a wide-eyed optimism that Loi cherishes more than anything other than persistence and wholesale dedication to work.

One of Loi's other graduate students is already well on her way to realizing part of Loi's preservation ethic. Debora Anzalone has documented and, working with other graduate students, begun the work of saving a rare sheep native to Abruzzo. These sheep, Pagliarola, have distinctive ears that stick straight out from the head, especially thick and curly hair, and a notoriously playful and friendly disposition. They were widely herded throughout Abruzzo, but they have disappeared over time. Families used to cherish them to the extent that they were rarely used for meat; they also were worth more as producers of cheese and wool. In the twentieth century, the wool market withered in the face of competition from other types of textiles, and the flocks of Pagliarola slowly began to disappear. Herds once numbering in the thousands dwindled, and now maybe sixty total individuals remain, most owned by a single shepherd. Once, shepherds led their flocks on extraordinarily long walks across the high Abruzzo mountains, crossing the region whose boundaries are now marked by national parks. Called the *transumanza*, the overland voyage moved sheep from higher elevations to lower valleys, but most of the passage remained high in the mountains. Stories of the *transumanza* have the status of old-time lore in parts of Italy, and heirs to the ancient crossings continue the tradition, albeit in much shorter distances. Still others lead tourists intent on reliving history.

Anzalone's work under Lino Loi, who is intent on changing the course of so many species headed toward extinction, may yet provide hope for a Pagliarola return to the highlands of Abruzzo. If so, there is likely also hope for Abruzzo's bears, who, hidden among the beech trees, watched generations of shepherds as they drove their flocks across the Abruzzi.

Loi's and his students' passion for the future and for science's limitless horizons is reminiscent of Carl Sagan's, and Loi speaks with the same earnestness and awe that the famous astronomer did. He says many times how beautiful science is and seems to humble himself before it, even if he is intellectually invested in its mysteries. He uses the phrase "beautiful mind" to describe scientists he admires, including colleagues and graduate students whom he clearly believes have a gift to share with the world. For Loi, a beautiful mind is a core trait of a great scientist. He insists on working only with the most driven, thoughtful, and courageous grad students in his lab because he wants them to have the passion, dedication, drive, and perseverance it takes to work on issues that may take decades to understand.

He has developed an unspoken process for vetting the students. He says if they ask him if they can work with them, he says no. But if they come back ten times, he knows they will be dedicated. The process replicates the nature of the work they will be doing. They will fail many times. They will proceed down a path only to be told "no" by some unforeseen circumstance or some unexpected feature of an otherwise inconsequential molecule. But failure can only be seen as part of the process, even a necessary part. The students cannot be put off by it. They must take risks, sometimes big ones, knowing that they will likely fail. In that failure, though, they will find beauty, new pathways, and unimaginable opportunities.

Loi's career has produced remarkable successes because he has endured countless invisible failures. And he finds beauty in that process. Those who have given up, either on their own work or on the science he is pioneering, represent, for Loi, the type who, lacking patience and perspective, cannot see how the past provides answers for the future. He calls them "fools," not angrily or self-righteously but with a tone of pity, even sympathetic understanding. They are fools because they have no resilience. Or vision.

# 29

~~~~~

# Ark

The University of Teramo has secured two male Pagliarola sheep, perhaps the last two males of the breed, loaned by the shepherd's family to the university with the hope that the animals may yet regain a foothold in the region. They are doted upon at the university, treated like celebrities, and graduate students readily show pictures of themselves tending to and playing with them.

As part of the plan to preserve the breed, Debora Anzalone and other graduate students, under the supervision of faculty advisors, used genetic testing to map the lineage of the two males. In doing so, they made a surprising discovery: One is actually the father of the other. The fact that the two sheep are so closely related means that they share DNA, which means in turn that the potential gene pool for reproduction is even more limited than previously thought.

Anzalone investigates ways to maintain this rare breed of sheep, and the first step is through securing DNA and semen samples. The collection of semen provides the foundation for any future work the lab might do; semen samples ensure that, even if the male sheep die, their DNA can be passed on when a female is made available.

The lab has collected 600 samples of semen and DNA, stored in various ways to ensure that if one method is not as durable over time, another method might be. The most well-known method is cryogenics, a process that involves freezing live cells. But Anzalone happens to be working in Loi's lab, and Loi, if nothing else, is unwilling to settle for standard procedures. When he began to see some of the limitations of cryogenics—whether the cost of the process or the equipment needed to do it properly—he decided a better process was needed. So his team adapted a process called ICSI to inject dry spermatozoa into the sheep oocytes.

Applying ICSI, or Intracytoplasmic Sperm Injection, across species is one of Loi's major innovations. When paired with processes like cryogenics, it provides a safety net to ensure preservation of DNA by hedging against something going wrong with any given sample or traditional methods of in vitro fertilization. The process involves securing semen, then selecting individual spermatozoa for preservation. The tail of the tadpole-like gamete is removed, which aids in the preservation because it results in only the head, which contains the DNA, entering into a state of suspended animation. That state is induced not through freezing but through freeze-drying. ICSI essentially dehydrates the sperm head; to bring it back to viability, scientists need only add water.

ICSI dehydration processes result in hardy, well-preserved DNA. The samples, which resemble small beads of Styrofoam, can be kept in small vials, even tossed around in a game of catch, with no damage to the DNA inside. The value of this process is hard to overstate. It provides a simple way to secure DNA for future generations, and the DNA is suspended in a state that is, simply put, easy to store and easy to resurrect. It is relatively cheap, can be replicated for species across the animal kingdom, and requires a less gentle touch than a process like cryogenics. It also, however, only allows for preservation of sperm. For preservation of other types of DNA, whether they be skin cells, kidney cells, or the cells from the placenta of a newborn child, different methods are needed, all of which require that cells be frozen.

Loi keeps frozen samples in what amounts to a modest DNA ark. In a room just across the hallway from the lab where he will be inserting roe deer DNA into the ovum of a sheep, a knee-high container resembling a propane tank for a home grill holds Loi's samples of life. When the top of the canister is opened, clouds of cold air billow out and cascade down the sides as though dry ice were melting. The opening, not ten inches in diameter, is ringed with a ridge, and from that ridge long, narrow, flat strips of metal hang down into the darkness inside. The top of the metal strips hook onto the ridge, but at the bottom, a curved hanger provides a hook for small bundles of vials. Inside those vials is life from around Italy. Rare sheep DNA, roe deer DNA, and others are all suspended inside the frozen chamber waiting to be reanimated.

Loi's ark is relatively new, but it was modeled after the Svalbard biological bank, which launched in 2006 and preserves plant seeds so that, if a species of plant disappears, a collection of its seed remains for future generations. Not long after Svalbard was established, the same idea was applied to animals. The Frozen Ark Project was established in the UK through the advocacy of a group of researchers at the University of Nottingham and has expanded into a consortium of arks spread around the world, representing what one commentator has called "the world's ultimate biological backup." Indeed, it represents the hope for what is now being called "de-extinction," essentially a reversal of a species' eradication. It might more accurately be called a resurrection.

Loi's involvement with cloning has provided him with motivation to be a leading force in de-extinction. He is inspired by the possibilities, but he has no illusions about its limits and challenges. He knows the technology still has far to go, and he understands that even just the idea of resurrecting species, let alone actually doing it, will be controversial. Still, he notes that first steps may include saving animals on the brink.

Among his colleagues' many priorities is the re-establishment of the white rhino in the wild. Two subspecies of white rhino exist; the northern white rhino has a population around 20,000, but the southern white rhino is guaranteed to be gone if a new technology does not come to its rescue. The last three—two females and one male—are all infertile, so the possibility of breeding them does not exist. Though all are in captivity and protected, there is no prospect of the species surviving past this last remnant.

Unless, of course, cloning works.

The cloning technology that might make cross-species cloning a reality will not require a fertile animal of the target species. All it requires is DNA from the species and, if Loi and his Vienna compatriots are right, a host animal.

Loi revels in a vision of animals returning. He sees an opportunity to reverse years of exploitation and degradation, and he sees profound beauty in the re-creation of life. One of his grad students, another of his "beautiful mind" prodigies, processes many of the samples and works on much of the data Loi collects. Marta Czernik works full-time in the lab. A Pole, she has been helping Loi with the group of Polish graduate students who came for a short course with him. They have come to work with Loi because of his progressive scientific agenda. Marta, with Domenico, Debora, and Luca, are the most recent students to work under and then alongside him, and they have helped develop the ark that now holds Loi's hope for the future.

It would be hard to overstate Loi's future-orientation, which drives him but also has given him perspective and appreciation for the eons of history that have shaped the natural world. That he imagines taking up archaeology in his retirement makes sense. His fascination with the past—whether human or animal—and with things deteriorating and being lost obscures, to some extent, a more passionate belief in the future. The result is a remarkable degree of patience grounded on a long view that assures him, on the one hand, of the significance of his work, but on the other hand, of the sheer audacity of it. It humbles him, even as it drives his ambition and work ethic.

"Look," he says, reflecting on one possible meaning of his work, "it is my obligation to future generations to preserve or help stabilize populations of animals." His eyes widen, and his hands open in front of him, elbows bent and palms toward his chest. "*We* can do something. So we must. If we know we can do something, we must. Others have other things they can do. *I* have this. *I* can do this."

Loi now sees in front of him the opportunity for something truly miraculous. If he brings new life to an animal that biology has hitherto taught should be rejected and destroyed by the mother's body, he will usher in a new era of animal science. He will also usher in hope for species like the white rhino, the Florida panther, and, of course, the Marsican bears. Abruzzo's bears live thirty-some-odd miles from his lab, and yet they may be as far away from him as the giant panda in terms of securing DNA. He has been blocked by bureaucratic red tape, incompetence, and, perhaps most of all, lack of vision.

"I just need some of the cells," he says. "Even from a dead bear— we just need some of its cells. A tiny piece to preserve so that when we finally know what to do, we can be ready."

He stands in a small courtyard adjoining his house. He lifts a glass of wine to his lips, takes a sip, then looks out over the valley that leads down to the sea. In the background, the Roman fountain trickles. A haze rises from the Adriatic. One of his cats rubs against his legs, and he reaches down to pet it, eyes still on the horizon.

"What's the harm?" he asks into the distance. "Why not preserve some cells?" He takes another sip of wine, sets down his glass, then, as though snapped out of a trance, he turns his attention to some bread in front of him. He rips a piece of it from the loaf and takes a bite. His eyes light up and he smiles. "We can do it. We can save them. The bears, the rhino. All of them." He pauses. When he resumes, he speaks with strength and certainty. "They don't have to disappear."

# PART VI: FATHER BEAR

# 30

## Champions

Germany's Museum of Man and Nature is located in Munich's Nymphenburg Palace, the former retreat of Bavarian aristocracy. The grand entrance to Nymphenburg faces east, with impressive palace wings curving slightly in toward the broad avenue approaching the central building. Stables rise up on the south wing, and in the north wing, through a small passageway that leads into a courtyard, is the museum's unassuming space. Tickets, a mere €3.50, are worth the price, if for no other reason than to see the museum's most famous display, sequestered away in a wide room on the second story of the building.

Up a staircase just past the ticket kiosk, the second floor of the museum opens into a series of rooms containing displays of all manner of animals, insects, and plants from around the world. Dioramas showing beasts in their natural habitats aim to educate museum visitors about the relationship among humans, animals, and the land, and taxidermied creatures are mounted to walls: a fish here, a raccoon there. Vitrines of insects or fossils and cabinets of curiosities fill floor space. Gemstones and colorful mineral samples gleam from behind glass.

Just past a chamber whose perimeter is stacked to the ceiling with glass boxes full of taxidermied large mammals, a four-sided enclosure rises up in the middle of a room, approachable from any direction. Inside the glass is a dramatic diorama of a snarling beast, one forepaw up; at the feet of the animal, the white box of an apiary is ripped open, and honey seeps out onto the ground. Plants, fur, and bees, dried and affixed to the hive, dot the display. Plastic vegetation, some blooming with spring color, is fixed to the ground, giving it the appearance of an alpine field. The great animal, a bear, stares out and up, its glass eyes surveying its surroundings.

Bruno, impressive even in death, rises like a king in his castle.

In the weeks after Bruno was shot, Germany announced plans to put him on display. The Museum of Man and Nature, housed since 1990 in the palace of Bavarian nobles, seemed an obvious place and provided much needed star power to the small organization. He remains the feature attraction of the museum.

Bruno is intentionally mounted near another bear in the collection. In the room adjoining Bruno's, the museum has on display a brown bear killed in Bavaria more than 150 years ago. He had been the last wild bear in Germany until Bruno crossed over from Austria. Now Bruno holds that distinction, as well as a far more dramatic display than his distant relative.

The killing of Bruno prompted worldwide controversy, and the mounting of him in a museum only exasperated the matter. His celebrity was so great that many outlets called his death an assassination, despite Bavarian officials' attempts to label it a public safety measure. Word of Bruno's demise spread across the newswires, and environmental groups from around the world expressed outrage and dismay. The word *murder* was commonly used.

The name of the person who pulled the trigger has never been publicly released. The outrage over the killing was so great that authorities refused to say who, exactly, shot Bruno. Death threats against the shooter, frequent at first, nonetheless continued for years.

Now, ten years after the order that ended Bruno's life, the shooter's identity is still kept under wraps.

One thing, however, is clear about the shooter: He or she was a masterful shot. Bruno died instantaneously. The precision hit that ended his life entered between his ribs and pierced his heart, and he was dead before he hit the ground. The shooter knew the stakes—the risk of being public enemy number one for years to come—and had to make sure the shot was perfect. It was.

The fact that Bruno did not suffer did not console many conservationists or Bruno's fans around the world. They called the shooting a tragedy and lamented the fact that a progressive nation such as Germany could not find a better solution than killing something they did not like and could not control. Some likened the action to state-sanctioned terror, an atrocity against life.

Germany's decision to put Bruno on display caused similar expressions of outrage. For animal rights activists, stuffing Bruno and propping him up behind glass transformed a tragedy into barbarism. While German officials insisted that Bruno could serve the country by helping educate schoolchildren and museum visitors, opponents insisted that mounting a dead animal accomplished precisely the opposite. They argued it illustrated that killing was the best method of controlling wild animals, and that, if anything, a Bruno display would glorify the state's power to eradicate endangered animals instead of preserving them.

Animal rights activists, however, were not the only ones outraged at Germany's plan to put Bruno on display. Italians, who had over the course of Bruno's adventures come to see him as one of their own, protested Germany's desire to keep him after he had been killed. They wanted him back on Italian soil.

The Italian government agreed. Referring to Bruno's remains, the Italian Minister of the Environment declared that "it cannot become a tourist attraction." German newspapers were swift to respond, calling on longstanding stereotypes of Italy being the land of scandal and lawlessness. Indeed, Bruno as an Italian bear fit conveniently into the narrative of Italy as a nation of thieves and petty criminals. *La Repubblica* responded in kind, noting latent prejudice in some of the German media and calling on Germany to return Bruno to the land where he was born. One opinion piece summarized it neatly: "We are back to the eternal conflict between Berlin and Rome, the legendary distrust of all time."

Italian furor grew, and German officials were caught in the midst of a public relations nightmare, the depths of which would not be fully known until 2010, when Julian Assange, the founder and figurehead of WikiLeaks, released a hoard of thousands of emails and classified communications. Most of them revealed the quotidian lives of bureaucrats, but among the stash are cables from American embassy staff and the US State Department. The State Department had been interested in Germany's handling of Bruno throughout the bear's increasing popularity, but his assassination and its resulting international conflict created even more interest among diplomats. WikiLeaks, known for exposing the dark secrets of governments, revealed in 2010 that Bruno was not only a hassle to Germans and a cause célèbre among Italians but also a lens through which US officials could view German negotiations of a policy debacle. The WikiLeaks documents show that a bear's impact crossed multiple international boundaries and occupied interest at high levels of German, Italian, and American governments.

The timing of Bruno's killing only exasperated matters. Four days after Bruno was killed, the World Cup offered up a subplot worthy of a Hollywood movie. Bruno was shot on June 26, and on June 30, both Germany and Italy won their respective World Cup matches to advance to the semifinals of the biggest sporting event on Earth. They happened to be in the same bracket. On July 4, they would face each other in an international showdown whose history, already steeped in deep rivalry, now included controversy. Bruno became a rallying cry for conservation-minded Italians.

Fans wore shirts that read, WE ARE ALL BRUNO, and others, as *La Repubblica* reported, adopted a more direct motto: AVENGE BRUNO. A longstanding anti-fur and animal rights organization called "The Lav" asked the Italian national soccer team to wear black armbands to show their solidarity with the bear and to signal to the world that their opponents were "barbarians." Protests and candlelight vigils were organized by environmental groups in small Italian towns and large cities alike, and even in Germany, protesters gathered in front of government offices to make their voices heard. When July 4 finally arrived, soccer fans and environmentalists united to cheer on the Italian team. One group of fans lifted a banner that read, WE ARE WITH BRUNO.

Germany was heavily favored to win the match. Not only was the country hosting the World Cup, but it had assembled a talented team of footballers. Younger and with a coach who preferred a more rapid pace of soccer than previous iterations of the national team, it had dazzled fans in its opening match and then continued to pile on victories. Italy, on the other hand, was a team drawn from a nation facing a soccer crisis. Local clubs had seen a spate of high-profile departures, and many believed Italy would bow out of the tournament early. Yet they rallied through the tournament to face their legendary foe. The winner would go to the championship game for a chance to bring home the ultimate sports prize, the World Cup trophy.

The game was nip and tuck, with neither team able to capitalize on the other's mistakes. At minute 118 of the game, though, Fabio Grosso, a player that few Italians even knew by name at the time, whipped the ball around a defender and chipped it into the corner of the net. Italian fans celebrated, and the host nation collapsed. In desperation to score, Germany's defense left too many gaps, and the Italians scored a second time in the closing minutes. It would be the Italians' final goal of the game but not of the tournament. Italy, ousting the host nation, would go on to win the World Cup.

Italy's fan base intermixed with Bruno defenders, and commentators on Italy's win over Germany readily noted it as a national vindication for Germany's mishandling of Bruno and his remains. One blogger summed up the experience of watching the game as a final triumph for the Italian bear: "Bruno won after all."

# 31

<hr>

# The Limits of Science

Early in his research, Paolo Ciucci realized that science alone was not going to save the bears of Abruzzo. In fact, the science of wildlife management suggests that ample space and resources already exist for the bears to thrive. Several studies, some based on fieldwork and some based on data modeling, have demonstrated that Abruzzo National Park, its buffer zone, and swaths of undeveloped land between Abruzzo and neighboring parks have enough space for a population of more than 100 bears. Much of the land between the Abruzzo, Gran Sasso, and Majella national parks already serves as virtual green corridors because they have not been developed. Bears can migrate essentially unmolested north and south, as well as eastward, without having to cross too many roads or encounter too many settlements. While certainly not the open wild of the western United States, it presents enough forest cover and nutrition to allow the bears to range and thrive. Not many years ago, one male even traveled as far north as Mount Sibillini National Park in Umbria. Not far from the historic town of Assisi, home of St. Francis, the great protector of wildlife, the bear roamed sections of Umbria and Marche for nearly four years before he finally returned to Abruzzo to mate. Space and habitat are not, at present, the most pressing issue for the bears.

People are. While the Camorra may be faulted for the sins of its ranchers, the real issue is the lack of public demand for change. Science, Ciucci and others like him know, will not address the problem of apathy about the bears.

So Ciucci has broadened his career and encouraged others to do the same. He has remade himself into a sociologist, cultural historian, and rhetorician. He understands that for his science to make a difference, he has to help people understand the significance of what is happening in Abruzzo. He has to make science understandable and urgent. He has to help people see what he sees when he goes into the field, talks to park officials, and runs complex data sets.

Ciucci's strength as a scientist comes not only from his keen observations of the natural world but also from his sense that science isolated from culture is a fool's paradise. It may be intellectually engaging, it may stir profound excitement in the mind and body, and it may even bring rushes of euphoria to practitioners who uncover mysteries or dare to test the boundaries of knowledge. But all of that is simply so much self-indulgent, even philosophical, chatter if it is divorced from the need to communicate with the world.

Ciucci has, accordingly, encouraged his students to engage with others, to learn to apply science in ways that are not only personally fulfilling but also relevant to people's lives. He nurtures, both in himself and others, a deep conviction that science matters and that the facts of the natural world must be known and understood before real change can occur. He conveys that by grounding his research in empirical data, verifiable evidence, and close observation and then forming relationships with others who can make change happen. That he has become so central to park bear policy is no accident. He did not conduct his research, publish it, and move on. Instead, he reached out to park management, conservation groups, and local stakeholders to help them understand precisely what his work meant for the region. That outreach has not only created change, it has brought hope.

The bears remain on a precipice. One catastrophic event could essentially doom the Abruzzo brown bears to extinction. But because Ciucci and others like him have finally shown precisely how precarious their position is, the path to safety is now clear. The problem is not nature's to solve. Indeed, the massive human migration out of rural Abruzzo into city centers during the twentieth century has provided, as Luigi Boitani has said, more opportunity than at any time in the last 100 years for the bears to expand their range. All that is needed is policing of crime and active combating of destructive practices. The protections already exist. Enforcement, to the degree that is needed, does not. To make that happen, a brighter spotlight needs to shine on the region, on the bears, and on the people who, by subtle activities at the periphery of the law, drive the bears over a cliff and into the abyss.

People like Ciucci are shining that spotlight. And people are finally seeing what he is illuminating, especially locally, where the risk to the bears is well known and, among many Abruzzese, an increasing concern. But more people in other parts of the world will need to experience Ciucci's vision in order for the bears to persist, and, as Ciucci well knows, it will likely not be scientists who can make that happen. It will be people like Bruno D'Amicis, the world-renowned photographer.

Ciucci and D'Amicis do not work together, at least not directly. Yet they aim for precisely the same thing. D'Amicis's training gives him keen insight into how Ciucci works, but D'Amicis, largely impatient with the creaking, slow processes of science-based policy change, knows he has a way to influence people's emotions on a far broader scale than scientific research is able to do. Ciucci works the system, changing it where he can and maintaining steady pressure on local government, the scientific community, and policy makers to attend to the results of his work. Ciucci makes Abruzzo's bears knowable. D'Amicis, turning his lens on the animals of Abruzzo, makes them approachable, relatable, and irresistible.

Together, Ciucci and D'Amicis form a kind of one-two punch in terms of Abruzzo bear preservation, even if they do so without intending it. D'Amicis's photographs, no matter how beautiful, need data to support their implied argument—that these animals need protection. Ciucci's data provides fuel for ensuring that the imagery of the bears finds its way into the public eye. With a coordinated effort, the park, local government, and groups like Salviamo l'Orso can ensure the bears thrive.

When Ciucci discusses the future, he is cautiously optimistic. He spends his weekends at a small apartment just outside a tiny village in the hills near Abruzzo, and there, he spends time writing, processing data, and advocating, often quietly working back channels like a diplomat to encourage change. When he takes breaks, he wanders out his apartment's front door and looks across a broad valley. Forests where an Abruzzo bear might easily roam roll over the top of hills and stretch out into valleys. In a nearby field, wildflowers, including a dazzling array of orchids that his wife has identified and documented, bloom and invite bees and butterflies. From here, the possibility of a bear recovery seems possible.

D'Amicis, not twenty miles away and looking out across the Sangro Valley from a hillside in Abruzzo National Park, can sense the same possibility. When watching cows graze within the park, he can feel overwhelmed by the looming loss, but in the mountains among the bears, his hope rekindles.

Early in 2016, standing at the edge of a cliff, he looked down into a pasture and saw one of the bears. It was a perfect day. Crisp winter air was giving way to spring warmth, and the field beneath him buzzed with new life. He brought his camera up, and through his lens, he saw something he had not initially noticed.

Cubs.

Two of them.

He tracked them with his camera, taking photos of them as they followed their mother. The family walked along the far side of the green field, up toward higher elevations and away from the livestock land below. One cub, bounding forward, tackled its sibling, and the two tumbled together, a ball of fur, a few feet down the slope. The mother paused a moment, swung her head to take a quick look, and then, like any parent, continued on her way knowing the cubs would shortly follow.

They did. They galloped up to her, and D'Amicis, lens ready, photographed the fleeting reunion, cubs gathering at their mother's great paws as she pressed forward toward a nearby forest. She nuzzled one, then glanced briefly around before disappearing with her young beyond the tree line.

In that moment, D'Amicis was overcome with emotion. He knows the bears are in trouble. He knows that their survival hinges on immediate action and a tremendous reversal of Italian policy and protection. He knows as well that complex forces are at work against them.

But, in that moment, he also knew something else.

He knew that the cubs he had just photographed were healthy and that there was at least one other, a third born that spring, who was roaming the park with his mother. He knew that they were safe, and he knew that for the moment, the bears had a future.

He knew because no one else had any idea that these cubs existed.

He was the first to see them, and he would keep them secret for a few more weeks in the hope of ensuring that they would not be the last of the bears of Abruzzo.

# Works Cited

The list below contains all sources referenced and also provides a broad overview of core issues and events in this book. Additional resources can be found at www.ewfthompson.com.

"Agguato mafioso a Giuseppe Antoci: vivo per miracolo [Mafia ambush on Giuseppe Antoci: I live by a miracle]." La7 Attualità. Video, 00:6:05. May 22, 2016. https://www.youtube.com/watch?v=i2vphsIXG7g.

Austrian Bear Emergency Team. "JJ1 'Bruno' in Austria and Germany 2006: Chronology and Risk Assessment." Vienna, Austria. doi: 10.13140/rg.2.2.17759.66726.

"Brown Bear Returns to Switzerland." *Swissinfo.ch.* June 5, 2007. https://www.swissinfo.ch/eng/brown-bear-returns-to-switzerland/5930790.

"Bruno Watch: 1-0 for Bavarian Bear as Finnish Hunting Dogs Can't Take Heat." *Spiegel Online.* June 13, 2006. http://www.spiegel.de/international/bruno-watch-1-0-for-bavarian-bear-as-finnish-hunting-dogs-can-t-take-heat-a-421257-amp.html.

"Bruno Watch: 'Problem Bear' Strikes Again." *Spiegel Online.* June 12, 2006.

Bethge, Philip. "The Great Bear Comeback." *Spiegel Online.* November 3, 2005. http://www.spiegel.de/international/spiegel/brown-bears-in-the-alps-the-great-bear-comeback-a-383038.html.

Blickenstaff, Brian. "Remembering Bruno, the Problem Bear That Overshadowed the 2006 World Cup." *Vice Sports.* July 8, 2016. https://sports.vice.com/en_us/article/aebez5/remembering-bruno-the-problem-bear-that-overshadowed-the-2006-world-cup.

Buck, Naomi. "Visitor Becomes Unbearable." *Globe and Mail.* June 17, 2006. https://www.theglobeandmail.com/incoming/visitor-becomes-unbearable/article18165514.

Cambone, Alberto, and Roberto Isotti. *Apennine Brown Bear: The Spirit of Wood.* Pescara: Carsa Edizioni, 2014.

Ciucci, Paolo, and Luigi Boitani. "The Apennine Brown Bear: A Critical Review of Its Status and Conservation Problems." *Ursus* 19, no. 2 (2008): 130–145. doi: 10.2192/07per012.1.

Ciucci, P., V. Gervasi, L. Boitani, J. Boulanger, D. Paetkau, R. Prive, and E. Tosoni. "Estimating Abundance of the Remnant Apennine Brown Bear Population Using Multiple Noninvasive Genetic Data Sources." *Journal of Mammology* 96, no. 1 (2015): 206–220. doi: 10.1093/jmamma/gyu029.

Ciucci, Paolo, V. Gervasi, J. Boulanger, T. Altea, L. Boitani, D. Gentile, D. Paetkau, C. Sulli, and E. Tosoni. "Ex post Noninvasive Survey of the Core Apennine Bear Population (Ursus arctos marsicanus) in 2014." Department of Biology and Biotechnologies, University of Rome. Project LifeNAT/IT/000160 "Arctos"—Action E3. February 2015.

Coen, Leonardo. "La contesa infinita dell'orso Bruno un'altra sfida tra Italia e Germania [The infinite contention of Bruno the bear: another challenge between Italy and Germany]." *La Repubblica.it.* July 4, 2006. http://www.repubblica.it/2006/05/sezioni/scienza_e_tecnologia/orso-germania/contesa-infinita/contesa-infinita.html.

Colangelo, Paolo, Anna Loy, Djuro Huber, Tomislav Gomerčić, Augustu Vigna Taglianti, and Paolo Ciucci. "Cranial Distinctiveness in the Apennine Brown Bear: Genetic Drift Effect or Ecophenotypic Adaptation?" *Biological Journal of the Linnean Society* 107, no. 1 (2012): 15–26. doi: 10.1111/j.1095-8312.2012.01926.x.

D'Amicis, Bruno, and Erik Baláž. *The Last Stronghold: Fifteen Years in the Company of Bears.* Italy: ADIN, 2011.

D'Amicis, Bruno. *Time for Wolves.* Rome: ORME Editori, 2015.

"Dario Febbo nuovo direttore del Parco nazionale d'Abruzzo, Lazio e Molise [Dario Febbo new director of the National Park of Abruzzo, Lazio and Molise]." *Greenreport.it.* November 21, 2011.

Di Leonardo, Federica. "Not Far From Rome, Italy's Distinct Bear Faces Down Extinction." *Mongabay* September 23, 2013. https://news.mongabay.com/2013/09/not-far-from-rome-italys-distinct-bear-faces-down-extinction.

Falcucci, Alessandra, Luigi Maiorano, Paolo Ciucci, Edward O. Garton, and Luigi Boitani. "Land-Cover Change and the Future of the Apennine Brown Bear: A Perspective from the Past." *Journal of Mammology* 89, no. 6 (2008): 1502–1511. doi: 10.1644/07-mamm-a-229.1.

Fenati, Massimo, and Adriano Argenio. "L'orso bruno Marsicano e la tubercolosi bovina [The Marsican brown bear and bovine tuberculosis]." April 2014. http://www.minambiente.it/sites/default/files/archivio/allegati/biodiversita/scheda_TTP_TBC_orso_bruno_marsicano.pdf.

Fraschilla, Antonio, and Alessandra Ziniti. "Messina, agguato a fucilate al presidente del Parco dei Nebrodi: salvo grazie all'auto blindata [Messina, ambushed to shot the president of the Nebrodi Park: except thanks to the armored car]." *Repubblica.it.* May 18, 2016. http://palermo.repubblica.it/cronaca/2016/05/18/news/ messina_agguato_a_fucilate_al_presidente_del_parco_dei_nebrodi_salvo_grazie_alla_blindata-140030429.

Gervasi, Vincenzo, Paolo Ciucci, John Boulanger, Mario Posillico, Cinzia Sulli, Stefano Focardi, Ettore Randi, and Luigi Boitani. "A Preliminary Estimate of Apennine Brown Bear Population Size Based on Hair-Snag Sampling and Multiple Data Source Mark-Recapture Huggins Models." *Ursus* 19, no. 2 (2008): 105–121. doi: 10.1093/jmammal/gyu029.

Hansen, Carla, and Vilhelm. *Petzi.* 42 Vols. Originally published as *Rasmus Klump* in 1952. First US volume published as *Barnaby Bear.* New York: Random House, 1979.

"Heat Turned Up on Bruno Bear." *Guardian.* June 18, 2006. https://www.theguardian.com/world/2006/jun/19/austria.mainsection.

Helm, Franz. "Feuer Buech." 1584. Rare Book & Manuscript Library, University of Pennsylvania, Ms. Codex 109.

"Italian Authorities Hunt for Killers of 3 Endangered Bears." *Pravda Report.* October 3, 2007. http://www.pravdareport.com/news/world/03-10-2007/98124-bears_killed-0.

Jennings, Christian. "Bears, Lynxes, Wild Horses and Wolves Return to Europe." *Newsweek.* December 6, 2014. http://www.newsweek.com/2014/12/12/bears-lynxes-wild-horses-and-wolves-return-europe-289216.html.

Landler, Mark. "Herr Bruno is Having a Picnic, But He's No Teddy Bear." *New York Times.* June 16, 2006. http://www.nytimes.com/2006/06/16/world/europe/16bear.html.

Lapinski, Mike. *Grizzlies and Grizzled Old Men: A Tribute to Those Who Fought to Save the Great Bear.* Guilford, CT: Falcon, 2006.

"Linea Verde: Intervista a Giuseppe Antoci [The Green Line: Interview with Giuseppe Antoci]." Rai Play. Video, 00:04:14. May 7, 2016.

MacDonald, Jake. *In Bear Country: Adventures among North America's Largest Predators.* Guilford, CT: Lyons Press, 2011.

McCracken, Harold. *The Beast That Walks Like Man: The Story of the Grizzly Bear.* Lanham, MD: Roberts Rinehart Publishers, 2003.

Meloro, Carlo. "Italy Has Its Own Subspecies of Bear—but There Are Only 50 Left." *Independent.* June 28, 2017. ttp://www.independent.co.uk/news/long_reads/italy-has-its-own-subspecies-of-bear-but-there-are-only-50-left-a7808156.html.

Payton, Brian. *Shadow of the Bear: Travels in Vanishing Wilderness.* New York: Bloomsbury, 2008.

Platt, John. "Extinction Likely for World's Rarest Bear Subspecies." *Scientific American*. May 6, 2011. https://blogs.scientificamerican. com/ extinction-countdown/extinction-likely-for-worlds-rarest-bear-subspecies.

"Poachers and Developers Threaten Bears' Survival: Italy." *NPIB* (Feb. 2005): 12–13.

Rubin, Alissa J. "Grin and Bear it? No Way, Germans Say." *Los Angeles Times* (Los Angeles, CA). May 26, 2006. http://articles.latimes. com/2006/may/26/world/fg-bear26.

Saragosa, Manuela. "How a Winemaker is Taking on Sicily's Rural Mafia." BBC News. July 25, 2017. http://www.bbc.com/news/ business-40645146.

"Sicilian National Park Boss Narrowly Escapes Assassination Plot by Mafia." *National Post*. May 20, 2016. http://nationalpost.com/news/ world/ sicilian-national-park-boss-narrowly-escapes-assassination-plot-by-mafia.

Slevert, James. "Italy's Leap Forward in Nature Protection Legislation." *The George Wright Forum* 15, no. 2 (1998): 43–49. http://www.jstor. org/stable/43597577.

Sommerhalder, Reno. *Ungezähmt: Mein Leben auf den Spuren der Baren*. Gockhausen: Worterseh Verlag, 2011.

———. *Unter Bären und Tigern: Mein Abenteuer in der sibirischen Taiga*. Gockhausen: Worterseh Verlag, 2014.

Squires, Nick. "Italy's Largest Animal Is On the Brink of Extinction." *Christian Science Monitor* May 3, 2011. https://www.csmonitor.com/ World/Global-News/2011/0503/Italy-s-largest-animal-is-on-the-brink-of-extinction.

———. "Sicilian Mafia Try to Assassinate Head of National Park in Night-Time Ambush." *The Telegraph*. May 19, 2016. http://www. telegraph.co.uk/news/2016/05/19/sicilian-mafia-try-to-assassinate-head-of-national-park-in-night.

Starr, Douglas. "The Lone Ranger." *Omni Magazine*. November 1989.

Tamahori, Lee, dir. *The Edge*. 1997; Fox, 2002. DVD.

Tarquinio, Gianluca. *Testimonianze Storiche Della Presenza Dell'Orso Bruno Marsicano in Abruzzo e Nelle Aree Limitrofe*. Sofa: Grafitalia, 2001.

Tassi, Franco. *Fauna Appenninica: I Protagonisti*. Castrovillari: Edizioni il Coscile, 2009.

———. *Orso Vivrai!* Milan: Editoriale Giorgio Mondadori, 1990.

———. *Parchi Nazionali in Italia: Alla Ricerca Della Nuova Arca*. Roma: Ente Autonomo Parco Nazionale D'Abruzzo, 1997.

Valentini, Maurizio, and Lucia Vaccarella. *Ritorni*. Self-published, Publish.it, 2016.

van Gils, Hans, Eduard Westinga, Marco Carafa, Antonio Antonucci, and Giampiero Ciaschetti. "Where the Bears Roam in Majella National Park, Italy." *Journal for Nature Conservation* 22, no. 1 (2014): 23–34.

# Acknowledgments

This book would have never existed without the generous sharing of time, leads, and resources of too many people to name, but I'm going to try nonetheless. Reno Sommerhalder helped launch me on the project way back in 2009, and Vladmira Lackova connected me with Bruno D'Amicis. Bruno, by sharing his time and energy over the years and by enduring my ongoing queries and requests, was an inspiration for this volume. Without him, this book would never have materialized.

I can think of no better model of a scientist than Paolo Ciucci, whose ability to synthesize material and convey it in understandable ways is matched only by his generosity and openness. Without his sharing of his Rolodex, this book would have floundered. His grace in handling the complexities of the bear issues in Abruzzo illustrates not only his love of wildlife but his understanding of human motives and reactions to difficult scientific discoveries. The bears could ask for no better advocate and friend. Lino Loi shares a similar awe and respect for both nature and science with Paolo, and Lino's generous spirit is perhaps best illustrated by his willingness to break bread with a complete stranger for no reason other than kindness and curiosity.

I'm deeply indebted to the many park staff and officials who agreed to speak with me, some in passing and some in depth. Dario Febbo made time on more than one occasion to visit and entertain my questions. He was generous with his time, good humored and tolerant of my questions, and willing to discuss personal matters that ultimately made this book both more meaningful and more accurate. Franco Tassi, whose story likely needs greater telling than can be offered here, handled my questions with openness and honesty, and his willingness to speak about his rich experiences suggest that his tenure as director still needs a full recounting. Daniela D'Amico facilitated contact with park officials, and Valentino Mastrella served as a thoughtful translator and interlocutor with many of PNALM's folks. If there have been any misunderstandings from our translated discussions, they rest solely with me.

Federica di Leonardo was an on-the-ground force without peer. Without her, interviews with key officials would have been impossible. She not only translated—both electronically and in real time—difficult conversations with federal, state, and regional officials, she also provided a web of connections, thoughtful guidance, and corrections on any number of matters. Mario Cipollone had insights that only foot soldiers in a war could have. He was kind enough to spend a day with me showing me some of the work Salviamo is involved in, and he clearly sees himself as not only a mentor to volunteers but also a grassroots activist with single-minded dedication to the cause.

I thank Franco Roberti, who took valuable time from his schedule to speak with me, as well as Fausto Cardella and other officials connected to investigations regarding organized crime. Their insights were invaluable, their work central to the health of the Italy. That people of such importance in the Italian government would offer their insights speaks to their intense professionalism.

My sincere gratitude to Geraldine McCarron and Marco Di Bona for their hospitality and conversation. They provided me with remarkable lodging, good food, and warm greetings at the end of each day. They offered helpful leads in my research and pointed me to fruitful interviews. Their hotel in Pescasseroli, Albergo Paradiso, provides the perfect base from which to explore PNALM and to which to retreat for a restful night after a day exploring the mountains. My thanks to Umberto at Wildlife Adventures and Paolo at Ecotur for useful discussions.

John and Midge were willing to take a risk on this book and provided support, encouragement, patience, and perspective throughout the entire process. Ashland Creek is a pleasure to work with, and I can't say enough about the service they provide in terms of bringing important stories about the natural world to light. Thank you.

My sincere thanks to various friends and family who read or discussed the project with me, including (but not limited to!) Tim Riemann, Bon Watkins, Michael Thompson, Jeremy Clement, Shannon Meehan, Charles McSoud, Ed Whittingham, Peter Poole, Scott and Tina Bryson, and many others, as well as my agent, Melissa Flashman, who helped read and shape early iterations of this book. My thanks as well to my colleagues at Stony Brook, and to Kristina Lucenko, who helped me secure funding for a portion of one of my trips. My nefarious colleagues from VMI have been steadfast supporters of my adventures and writing, and they always deserve my thanks. My deep gratitude, admiration, and love for Barbara Crawford and Mario Pellicciaro, whose friendship, encouragement, and introduction to Italy paved the way for this book. My parents fostered in me an inquisitiveness and eagerness to see the world, traits that are the foundation of this book, and Laura endured my many trips and nights writing, and I'm grateful for her support. My brother spent many nights with me in a tent in all sorts of wild places, and I'm thankful for his constant queries. My son, every month for years when this book stalled, persisted in reminding me of the hope for the bears and my obligation, having heard their story, to try to share it. This book is for him in the hope that the wild finds its way into his heart.

# About the Author

Roger Thompson is an award-winning nonfiction writer and director of the Program in Writing and Rhetoric at Stony Brook University. A former wilderness canoe guide for a Minnesota camp and the founder and director of an environmental program in Banff, AB, he currently lives in New York with his wife and son.

## Ashland
## Creek
## Press

Ashland Creek Press is an independent publisher of ecofiction, which includes books in all genres about animals, the environment, and the planet we all call home. We are passionate about books that foster an appreciation for worlds outside our own, for nature and the animal kingdom, and for the ways in which we all connect. To keep up-to-date on new and forthcoming works, subscribe to our free newsletter by visiting www.AshlandCreekPress.com.

CPSIA information can be obtained
at www.ICGtesting.com
Printed in the USA
FFOW02n1527080718
47320732-50332FF